TALES OF THE

TALES OF THE CUT

Carl Leckey MBE

Léonie Press

ISBN13: 978-1-901253-52-8
ISBN 1 901253 52 X
First published November 2005
Reprinted December 2005
Reprinted October 2006
Reprinted March 2010
Reprinted October 2011

British Library Cataloguing in Publication Data.
A catalogue record for this book is
available from the British Library.

Published by
Leonie Press
13 Vale Road, Hartford
Northwich, Cheshire CW8 1PL
Great Britain
Tel: 01606 75660   email: anne@leoniepress.com
website: www.leoniepress.com

Cover illustration by Patricia Kelsall

Printed by Poplar Services, St Helens
Cover lamination by The Finishing Touch, St Helens

About the author

CARL LECKEY is the youngest of three children. He grew up in wartime Britain and loved the excitement of having Italian prisoners of war in the area. His time as a child was spent collecting shrapnel and clambering around the shipwrecks on the shore of the Mersey.

One of his favourite places was his grandfather's allotment where old comrades from the 1914-18 conflict would meet in the garden shed to share a drink and a smoke. They would reminisce and talk through the horrors of what they had experienced in the Great War. If a boy kept quiet, he could hear all sorts of things to fire the imagination.

Carl served on the Mersey tugs for 15 years with a break for two years' National Service in the Army from the age of 19 to 21. On returning to the tugs he rose to the rank of Mate, before being made redundant at the age of 30 in 1968 when the company was taken over.

He then worked as a Leading Lock-Keeper for British Waterways in Cheshire for 28 years until ill-health brought premature retirement. He was a Union Steward Convenor, and Worker

Representative on the Company Pension Fund Management Committee.

In 1985 he was awarded a Winston Churchill travelling Fellowship to study Ports and Harbour Services on the Mississippi and Yangtze Rivers in the USA and China. On returning from his travels he undertook a series of lectures on his experiences abroad to interested organisations.

In 1995 he was awarded an MBE by the Queen for services to British Waterways.

After retiring and finding time on his hands, armed with a computer, Carl completed a writers' course with the Open College of Arts. He has had a few short articles accepted for the works magazine, newspapers, and a boating magazine. He also writes articles for shipping magazines and historical organisations. In 2004 Carl had his first full-length novel *The Angels of Mons* published in New Zealand. One of his poems was the editor's choice in a competition organised by the International Library of Poetry.

He was married to Rose in 1961; their two children and four grandchildren are now New Zealanders.

He has always been the storyteller of the family, and loves to collect interesting tales and unusual happenings.

Carl says: "Truth is stranger than fiction – I have had no need to make up many of the events described, but I have changed the names of the people involved, rolled several characters together and toned down some of the more colourful language that's used as a matter of course in the all-male working environment of the waterways..."

Contents

Ready for the latest Big Debate

Carl's 'sculpture' at Dutton Locks (see page 11)

Chapter One
'Arry the boatie and others

DURING MY CAREER as a lock-keeper and a workers' representative, I came across many colourful characters on the waterways. I began collecting stories at the time and taking notes. I
wasn't sure what to do with them but when I had to take early
retirement I decided to write about them.

The tales in this book are based on my own story and that of
many other canal workers.

Two of the most outstanding of these characters were 'Arry and
his poor long-suffering wife Cissie. I worked with him and dealt
with his problems and the ones he created for about a 20-year
period. I can assure the reader they astounded me by their odd
antics on every occasion when we met. There are many legends
about these two individuals I did not personally witness that are
more colourful than those I have recorded, but that's another
story. Here are a number of my encounters with 'Arry and some
of his mates.

Both 'Arry and his wife Cissie were born on narrowboats when
families lived aboard the craft they worked. Cissie was born on a
boat in the canal basin at Stourport on Severn, with no medical
assistance other than an old canal boat woman who delivered her.

'Arry always reckoned he was neither a Cheshire nor a
Shropshire man, as his mother began giving birth in the boat
cabin whilst in one county. She finally delivered him in the next
county as the horse-drawn boat continued on at its walking-pace
voyage. He once revealed this fact to me after a particularly heavy

1

drinking bout when sentimentality was inclined to prevail in his nature and truths were outed.

Because of the unusual circumstances surrounding his birth, his parents wanted to celebrate the fact by naming him Shropchess or Cheshrop. It appears the vicar who christened him would not agree to this arrangement and named him Harry after his father – or 'Arry to his friends and workmates.

Presumably vicars had the power to do this when he was christened.

When he was around five years old – 'Arry was not sure of his age – his mother died. Being the youngest of the brood the young boy became surplus to requirements without his mother to look after him. His father could not cope with a young non-productive child in the confines of the narrowboat home and placed the young lad in an orphanage. His father still lived on and worked a pair of boats with the assistance of 'Arry's older brothers and sisters. All went fairly well in the orphanage until he was introduced to a village school. The other kids didn't like 'Arry and made his life hell – calling him 'the dirty boatie Gypo', amongst other insults. He couldn't grasp the learning process and was continually picked out and humiliated by the teachers. Finally they gave up any pretence of trying to teach him and usually left him to his own devices. He was given menial jobs like picking up litter or tidying the gardens with the caretaker. Things began to look up for the lad when the local squire, one of the school governors, seemed to take a shine to him on founder's day. When 'Arry was about eight years old he was selected to take part in a very important ceremony, named the beating of the bounds. 'Arry felt very proud but had no idea what it was all about. The other older kids who had experienced the ceremony on previous occasions were no help and sniggered whenever he asked them to explain what it meant. Come the big day 'Arry was dressed in his best Sunday clothes and followed a parade led by the local dignitaries. As he proudly marched along he noticed the squire carried the cane that usually hung behind the schoolmaster's desk. This fearsome instrument was usually suspended on the wall in full sight of the pupils as a dire warning not to misbehave.

'Arry had experienced the cane on a number of occasions and hated the sight of the object. But for some reason he couldn't figure, the squire now carried it. The lad watched the other kids pointing at the dreaded cane then at him and sniggering whilst simulating arse swipes. He overheard the squire talking to the mayor and they were discussing how many stations they had to cover.

"Funny," thought 'Arry, "I didn't know there was more than one railway station close to the village."

Eventually they arrived at a crossroads and the parade came to a halt in front of a large boulder. The squire made a speech, the mayor made a speech, the members of the parade hip, hip, hoorayed. 'Arry still couldn't figure out what it was all about but realised the ceremony was coming to a climax. The teacher pushed 'Arry forward and instructed him to bend over and touch the rock. Reluctantly complying with these strange orders, but reassured by his friend the squire, the lad reluctantly obeyed the order.

His reward for his compliance was a resounding thwack on his backside.

His howl of protest was immediately followed by another accurately administered thwack. This time his screech of pain was mingled with the cheers of the assembled delighted villagers. This final blow was enough for 'Arry; convinced this was not a good place to be amongst the mad yokels, the bewildered lad took to his heels and ran. Eventually after many dodges he finally evaded his enraged pursuers. He made his way to the nearest canal that passed through the outskirts of the village. He hid in the canalside bushes until a pair of horse-drawn trade boats approached. Thankfully 'Arry recognised an uncle leading the horse. He dropped alongside and explained what had happened to him, whilst pleading to be saved from the mad villagers.

The sound of the villagers' voices grew closer before the uncle would allow him to slip aboard the boat and hide himself under a hatch cover. His uncle, a shrewd character, saw the chance of cheap labour and granted 'Arry sanctuary on the understanding that he worked for victuals only. That episode ended his education, as he never attended a school again.

The lad gratefully accepted the conditions and stayed with his uncle as a virtual slave until about a year later when they crossed paths with 'Arry's father. His father greeted his son with a sound beating for running away, punched the uncle on the nose for exploiting the lad, and demanded payment for the time 'Arry had spent working for him.

Chapter Two
Out of the frying pan into the fire

HIS FATHER TURNED out equally as bad as his miserly uncle, and made 'Arry work for him until the age of fourteen. On coming of that age and considered to be a man, he was given his own butty boat as a reward for his labours by his grandfather who retired from the cut. Unfortunately, the deal was a partnership with an elder brother who turned out to be as bad as his father. He worked 'Arry day and night for little reward despite the so-called partnership. It took him a few more years and the arrival of World War Two before he was able to get command of a pair of boats working for a well-known carrying company. After the war the boats were nationalised by the government of the day. 'Arry was incorporated into a state-owned company along with his boats. For the first time in his life he enjoyed regular pay and holidays and other benefits he had only dreamed of in the past.

'Arry had an accent hard to define. His deep voice reflected the many places and people he associated with during his boating days, due to the nomadic existence on the canals his employment entailed. I observed that his accent depended on whom he worked with. He spoke Brummy with Birmingham men and Scouse with Liverpool lads.

Even though he had no schooling I would challenge anyone to outsmart him in a deal. I personally witnessed him being outwitted by a farmer on one occasion, but he repaid the man eventually. The fool had injured 'Arry's pride in front of his mates. Although the revenge took time to complete, like a Mafia vendetta, it had to be carried out. Honour had to be satisfied.

5

Another form of pride with 'Arry and amongst most of the men born on the narrowboats was education. Although many of them couldn't read or write, they would not openly admit it especially in front of other boaties. I have actually witnessed one man pretending to read a newspaper although he held it upside down. Another ex-boatie would have his children outline the stories and headlines before he left home for work of a morning. On arrival, usually at baggin time, he would pretend he was reading from the daily paper in front of his mates. The more literate of us knew this was a charade, but never let on and enjoyed the daily spectacle. Who were we to embarrass a man because we, the fortunate, had the ability to read?

I once sold 'Arry fifteen hens. The deal to sell was struck in the late afternoon as he finished work. The next morning when he returned he brought the cash to settle what he termed his 'owings'.

The arrangements for transporting the birds had been sorted the day before on the way home. No doubt some form of inducement had been agreed with the regular driver. He was to take the hens home with him at the end of that day in the works bus.

A spit on the hand followed by a handshake sealed the deal.

'Arry had knocked off at noon and was eating his butties sitting on an oil drum inspecting the hens when I went to collect the eggs from the chicken coop. He sat quietly watching until I came out of the pen with a basket of eggs.

As I closed the gate he remarked admiringly, "Nice eggs."

"Yes," I replied. "Good layers, nice big brown 'uns."

"What would you pay for them in the shops?" 'Arry questioned.

"I think about five bob a dozen for good 'uns like these. That would be about right," I hesitantly ventured, suspecting some kind of trap. He didn't disappoint me.

"Well," he thought for a moment scratching his stubbly chin. "Seeing as I know you, I'll let them go for four bob a dozen."

I was flabbergasted for a while.

"*My* hens," he added. "*My* eggs."

6

He chuckled with delight at his own cunning.

It must have been one of my better days, because a sudden inspiration struck me how I could outwit the old villain – a hard task to achieve.

I retorted, "You're right, 'Arry, four bob is a good price."

He smirked with glee and as he stood up from his makeshift seat, stretched out his grubby hand for the cash.

"Ah! But?" I continued. "I reckon bed and breakfast, and an evening meal, plus a day's lodging for fifteen hens, works out about four bob – so I reckon we are about even."

'Arry grimaced his toothless smile.

My small victory went down in the annals of canal history to be retold in an exaggerated form for years around cabin stoves at baggin time.

Though he did not like to lose out on a deal, especially to be outfoxed by one he considered a townie, he appreciated a smart opponent. Although he wouldn't admit defeat, the twinkle in his watery eyes told another story. No doubt the second he lost out he was planning his revenge on me at a later date.

At knocking-off time the bus arrived with eleven of his work-mates already seated aboard, impatient to be on their way home.

'Arry approached the driver's window. It was not the same man he had made arrangements with to transport the hens home.

"All right if I put a bit of gear on to take home?"

The driver nodded his consent, not quite sure what he was letting him self in for. As an afterthought he warned 'Arry, "As long as it's not knocked-off gear?"

'Arry assured him with an injured tone, "Would I do that?" as he moved around to the rear of the vehicle.

He had previously captured the hens and had them penned in my stock trailer. He manhandled the trailer until it virtually touched the rear of the vehicle.

'Arry took up position and banged on the door until one of the passengers opened it, whereupon 'Arry handed him a hen.

"'Ere lad," he ordered. "Pass this bugger up the bus."

He had instructed me to enter the trailer and pass the hens to him when he requested. He continued with this practice until each protesting passenger carried a hen on his knee.

Why, you may ask, would the rest of his workmates go along and accept these odd travelling companions without moaning? Because almost all of them depended on 'Arry in some way or another, that's why.

'Arry, this English version of a Mafia Godfather, had his mates sewn up.

Eventually he climbed aboard himself and slumped into his usual seat at the back of the bus. When he was settled he ordered me to hand him the large cardboard box.

My new TV had been delivered in the box that morning – it now contained the remaining hens. He was in the process of heaving it up to place it on his knee for the journey home when I slammed the back doors of the bus shut.

It was as they started off that disaster struck. The bottom fell out of the box. The startled hens made a break for freedom within the confines of the bus. Chaos reigned on board. The vehicle stopped then jerkily started again a couple of times. Eventually the van proceeded on its way encouraged by 'Arry's shouts of "Stop yer bleedin moaning or we'll never get 'ome. They're only a few hens, for Jesus' sake."

As an added inducement for his workmates' co-operation he generously offered, "If they lay on the way home, youse can 'ave the eggs for nowt."

The driver protested, with a hen firmly ensconced on the top of his industrial helmet.

One of the lads shouted between bouts of laughter, "Bloody hell, Steve, you look like one of those First World War German generals."

He was not amused.

"What if they crap?" he complained.

'Arry roared, "You can 'ave that for nowt as well."

The poor driver could not shake the nickname of 'Kaiser Bill' after that incident.

One of the lads described the journey home to me next day. It had taken them twice the normal time to complete the trip. The pantomime only finished when they dropped 'Arry and his remaining hens off at his cottage. During the journey three of the hens had escaped through the driver's window when he opened it to try to rid the van of the smell. They were last seen happily pecking away on a traffic island in the busy centre of town. Despite 'Arry's pleas to be given the chance to recover the escapees, Steve continued on his way. They left chaos behind them as other drivers couldn't believe their eyes when they recognised the birds as hens.

I only knew 'Arry when he finished working the carrying boats and became as he termed it, a 'shore worker' on the canals. His main job was a general labourer, usually delivering piles, cement, and so on, by boat to gangs working up and down the cut. Now and again through sickness or holidays he was seconded onto other gangs despite many objections from the permanent workers. Although he worked a company boat, to all intents and purposes it belonged to him. The management even referred to the craft as "Arry's boat'. When he reluctantly handed it over when going on holiday, he left a string of orders with his relief.

Woe betide them if anything was amiss when he returned.

Most of his so-called working day he spent wheeling and dealing with pleasure boat owners, ships' crews, his workmates and farmers. At mealtime he cleared and reset his snares and went on mooching expeditions.

Stowed aboard his boat were snares, traps and other assorted trading goods. I once likened him to one of the old sailing ship captains that traded mirrors and beads to the natives of Africa. 'Arry quite liked this description of his enterprises.

Another presumably rewarding enterprise 'Arry undertook was tapping the maple trees lining the river and canals, recovering his catching bottles on a regular basis. We never figured out what he did with the prized contents, as he wouldn't divulge the secret to us and never offered it as part of a deal.

When he joined his workmates for the run home in the works bus was the time when he did much of his business. Rabbits, hares, pheasants and grouse, with an odd stray hen, goose or duck were all part of his trade goods. In the season he dealt in all the seasonal fruit, purloined mostly from canal and riverside orchards – not forgetting potatoes and other veggies that grew in fields along the cut.

While lying at the lock he had the opportunity to deal with the crews of the big barges and ships that traded up the river from the docks and foreign countries.

The sight of the old rogue negotiating a deal with a non-English speaking seaman was great entertainment for the rest of the lads. Somehow the deals were struck, with 'Arry usually coming out on top with a victorious smirk on his stubbly face.

Another fact about 'Arry came out when I received a parcel off a foreign ship. We had always suspected he had the digestion of a hyena and he proved it on a particular summer day.

All lock, bridge and employees' cottages at that time received an annual issue of coal. This was a delivery job that 'Arry particularly enjoyed.

The coal gang consisted of seasonal workers, mostly students along with some of his boatie mates. 'Arry and his gang also delivered coal to the assorted company craft on the river and canals.

They did all the work while 'Arry carried on his trade with the housewives.

A coaster arrived and the cook offered me a large bag of assorted meat for the lock dogs. He explained he'd had trouble with his freezer and it kept switching on and off. He suspected the meat had gone off and wasn't fit to eat – it was "a bit green." He pointed out, "The stuff might not be even fit for the dogs. I wouldn't want to make them ill."

Before the rabies laws were enforced most of the ships that visited the river carried their own dogs. The Danish seamen were very fond of the dogs on the lock, always bringing them titbits and making a fuss of them whilst in the lock. The dogs themselves became very shrewd and knew instantly which ships fed them well. Before the generous ships actually entered the lock the dogs would be ready and waiting for their perks.

The Panamanian registered ships hardly fed their crews, never mind the dogs. How the dogs knew the difference amazed us but they did without fail.

The cook handed me the bag of meat. I told him I would check it out and maybe I would just dump the lot if it looked bad. I took the meat over to the lock hut to leave there while I sorted out a couple more ships that were due to lock through. It was an unusually busy day on that occasion. I told my mate we would divide the meat between us for the dogs if it was fit. 'Arry was in the hut eating his baggin with a couple of his mates. Always with an eye to a deal he spotted the bulging bag and asked me, "What's in the bag then, eh, pal?"

I was on the phone to the next lock when I answered, "Oh, a load of meat off the ship, the cook just gave it me to share…"

At that moment another ship blew and I rushed out of the hut to get the lock ready without finishing the sentence. It was an hour or so before I returned to the hut.

A funny thing happened as we finished with the last ship. As she was leaving the lock the pilot hailed us; from his vantage point high up on the ship's bridge he had spotted what he believed was a body in the reeds above the lock. My mate was all for ringing the police but I had recently made a fool of myself with them when one of the lads had pulled a bottle out of the river containing a note. It stated a girl was being held prisoner on a yacht somewhere on the river. After an intensive search the police discovered the bottle had been thrown into the river by a certain lock keeper's daughter as part of a game she was playing with her pals. Needless to say the police were not that pleased with me. I decided on this occasion I would investigate before notifying them.

My mate and I sculled the cock boat to the place the pilot indicated. After pushing nervously through the reeds we found the bottom halves of two shop window mannequins, much to our relief. They had evidently been thrown into the river and drifted down in the last flood, finally lodging in the reeds when the water was higher than normal. We dragged them into the boat and took them back to the lock for disposal.

A couple of days later I had a school party visiting the locks, which was a regular occurrence in those days. For a joke I dressed the dummies and located them amongst some of the spare machinery on the lock side. The kids loved them and so I left them

11

there for the next visit. From then on they became a regular feature of the locks. The visiting public admired them and many had their photographs taken alongside the legs – they were even featured in a magazine as a sculpture.

One evening the local cruise boat came through carrying a party of visiting Americans. I heard the skipper explaining to one of the passengers that the sculptor was the lock-keeper. He directed him my way. When he introduced himself he asked me to interpret what the display meant. I never thought anyone would consider it a serious piece of art.

Rather than disappoint him by revealing that I'd dressed the dummies and placed them amongst the junk to entertain the kids, and that the piece of loose chain I'd draped around them was to stop the wind blowing the figures over, I jokingly invented a complicated story about them. I explained the figures in the display were attempting to escape from the bondage of cares and woe, and were being held by the chains of mortgages, debts, family commitments, etc etc. He listened intently. When I finished, he stuck out his hand, shook mine, then congratulated me.

"Son!" he said, "I see exactly what you mean. Your sculpture portrays it perfectly. That could very well be me since I got married for the third time."

The rest of the passengers had been listening to our conversation and broke into spontaneous applause.

The exhibit? Well, it remained on site until I retired, then it was removed by a person who was not an admirer of art and was devoid of a sense of humour.

In the meanwhile I had acquired two complete female mannequins contributed by a well-wisher. We have them located in our garden at the locks sitting amongst the flowers on garden benches during the summer months. It's amazing how many times the Dutton Dolls are admired and photographed.

But back to the coaling gang...

After recovering the part-mannequins I approached the lock hut to detect the smell of cooking wafting out of the open window. When I entered the hut the coal gang were just finishing a banquet of steaks, bacon, liver and kidneys. In fact the hungry buggers had consumed the lot. They sat around with bloated bellies burping with self-satisfied smirks on their faces. My mate and I looked on the scene with horror. I didn't have the heart to tell them why the cook had given me the suspect meat – they looked so contented. All day we expected them to collapse with food poisoning but they survived. Maybe the years of living on the boats with no fridge had given them cast-iron stomachs? From what I have learned about students they seem able to consume anything, as well. But maybe it's just as well the poor dogs' digestions weren't challenged by the stuff.

We have had a number of dogs over the years since I have resided on the waterways. The dog I brought with me to my lock house in the Sixties had the name of Yogi. He was a rat bag of a dog with a majority portion of Bearded Collie in his make-up. I had trouble with Yogi the Untrainable Dog from the beginning, after he was foisted on me by my parents when they found him unmanageable. When he made one of his frequent breaks for freedom there was only one way to capture him. I had to start the car whereupon he would jump in (expecting to go for another tour around the country barking and challenging all and sundry to battle) and then I could snap his lead on.

Apart from his visions of being the supreme fighting dog he was a great lover given the opportunity – and this appeared to be often in his case, when the resulting look-alike dogs started appearing in the district. Opposite our flat there resided a lovely looking bitch by the name of Quinnie. She had beautful golden fur and big 'come-to-my-basket' eyes a randy dog would die for. She was Yogi's heart's desire, along with every other male dog in the district. An unfortunate pug with only three legs also lived nearby. His master, being a skilled cabinet-maker, had fashioned an artificial back leg that he strapped to the poor pug. Quinnie was always protected from the villainous pack of assorted would-be lovers that assembled when she came into season. Pug lurked close at hand but never participated in the fights that took place frequently for Quinnie's affection.

One day her mistress didn't latch the door securely; the wind blew it open and Quinnie escaped to confront her assembled admirers. Instead of doing what a dog should do in these circumstances the pack began to fight. There was much snapping of teeth, yelps, barks and cowering away by the defeated with tails between legs.

I observed the melée from a safe distance from the upstairs window of our flat. There was no way I was admitting to owning Yogi. I suspected he would be heading for another great victory. He was proving that the strongest dog wins the paw of the fair maiden. One more to go! Yogi pinned his opponent to the ground, bared his fangs and threatened to rip his throat out if he did not depart in haste. The defeated cur slunk away and Yogi turned to claim his reward. Too late. Too late. Peg-leg, despite his disability, had beaten him to the prize. I swear I saw a grin of triumph on that dog's face, if this is possible.

I considered taking Yogi to the vet's for the snip. I even got as close as the door to the surgery but couldn't bring myself to have my pal deprived of something I should hate to lose myself. I turned back at the very gates of hell and Yogi remained intact. He never knew how lucky he was that day.

Anyway, there I go deviating again.

We moved to the locks soon after the incident. He didn't change in any way but I thought that when he was out in the country miles from anywhere we would have no more problems. All that happened was that he roamed further and further in his quest for likely bitches.

I once had a good friend Jan who was a Danish captain. He owned his ship and lived on board with his wife and their prize poodle Olga. They had no children and they treated the dog as if she was their daughter. I have to point out he *was* a friend until Yogi besmirched the reputation of his beloved Olga. Jan had been away with his ship working the Black Sea ports for more than two months. The night before he sailed he moored overnight at the locks and we had a little party aboard his ship. When I received orders that he was coming back for a cargo I was looking forward to seeing him and his wife again. Before he actually came into sight he began to berate me in a mixture of English and Danish on the ship-to-shore radio. It was only when he moored in the lock that I discovered the source of his anger. His beloved Olga had given birth to five lovely pups a couple of days before. It was either a miraculous conception or she had been got at – and he blamed Yogi. I have no idea how or when it happened for the ships were normally only in the lock for about ten minutes. Usually our dogs were more occupied eating titbits, but maybe on one occasion Yogi had had other things on his mind.

Despite his initial anger Jan and his wife kept the pups until they could leave their mother. At that stage they were definitely identifiable as Yogi's offspring. When he cooled off and we became friends again he admitted that he only parted with the pups to dog lovers who cared. Mostly they consisted of lock-keepers or dock workers. Yogi's descendants are spread as far as Ireland, Finland, Denmark and other places in Europe. Not bad for a rat bag with no pedigree – but I hope his offspring are better-behaved than their father.

I tried to figure out how and when the nuptials had taken place. The night before Jan sailed on the long voyage, when my wife and I attended his party, to my knowledge Yogi was secure in the house. But we did have two kids at the time prone to leaving doors open and telling porkpies to cover their misdemeanours. After the little affair with Olga the lads renamed Yogi as 'Flash'.

He never changed until the day he died – even when he was deaf and nearly blind he would still challenge visiting dogs to a scrap. Flash's appetite for his other hobby appeared to wilt with age or maybe he just forgot what to do and how to do it. Old age comes to all of us eventually.

I don't fight any more, either.

Pooh One was my mate's dog but was shared by everyone. A Labrador originally called Set, he acquired his second name from one of his more noxious afflictions. He actually believed he was the lock-keeper and we were his assistants. He loved having the gangs of men working on the locks, and spent his time amongst them. He shared their baggin and even sat in on the card games that took place at meal times. The lads loved him when they worked on the lock machinery and he sat overlooking the job like a foreman. On one occasion the lads dressed him up in a leather jacket, an industrial helmet and goggles. He never objected and wore the gear until the end of the work day. If we locked a ship or barge through during darkness he would carry a torch around in his mouth as he attended to his duties, only dropping it to consume his perks. His favorite trick, when he considered the lads had been too long in the lock hut, was to run in with a long handled brush and scatter all and sundry. We were all broken-hearted when he passed away with kidney problems.

Pooh Two was also my mate's dog but he spread his affection amongst all of us. A Labrador/Spaniel mix, Pooh Two was a great hunter and regularly delivered a dead rabbit to us in the lock hut. A lovely good-natured dog and constantly hungry, he didn't always wait to be fed by the ship's crew. He went aboard the ship in the lock and knew where the galleys were located. We reckoned he personally knew all the ships' cooks by name and never failed to get the choice titbits when he jumped aboard.

We discovered him missing on one occasion: he was traced at the last lock still aboard the ship, just as she was about to leave. Needless to say he was in the company of the Filipino cook. Sadly Pooh Two disappeared without trace. We spent days searching for him to no avail. We believe he jumped ship and ran away to sea to be close to the source of the bones rather than waiting for them to be delivered.

Pooh Three was my mate's dog. He was a wonderful, peaceful mutt without an enemy in the world and is sadly missed, as were his predecessors.

It was hard to tell what breed he was. He had portions of all kinds in his make-up. One thing was certain – he was a big dog that hated water. He also had ambitions to eat himself to death and consumed anything and everything. The foreign seaman loved him and saved huge bagfuls of scraps collected during the voyage. Like Pinocchio's nose he growed and growed, and despite our efforts to control his diet he finally expired at the age of eight with a size similar to a baby hippo. He had developed the same traits as Pooh One and became a lock-keeper, attending every locking.

This was the last dog belonging to my mate that we classed as a lock dog; soon after he died the last ship navigated the river. No more waiting for bones.

Barnacle Bill was adopted by my mate. She chose her friends and would not tolerate enemies on her patch. A combination of all kinds, she answered to the name of Barney. Although the dog had a male name she was a bitch – a mistake made by the seamen who rescued her. When the mistake was discovered they decided it was too late to change her name. She had been saved by the ship's crew amongst the flotsam in a corner of Dublin docks as they painted the hull using the ship's lifeboat. Some horrible person had thrown a bag full of newly-born pups into the dock. The crew saw movement, pulled the bag out of the water and landed it on the ship. Barney was the sole survivor of five tiny blind pups. The crew hand-reared her and she quickly repaid their kindness by assuming responsibility as watchkeeper whenever they went ashore. The captain told us she was so good at her job she would not let anyone other than the crew aboard the ship. This included the Customs – much to the amusement of the crew. She went away to sea for many years but eventually had to swallow the anchor and become a landlubber on the locks when the rabies law was strengthened. My mate adopted her as company for his other dog, Pooh. As a pair they made a great hunting team and could catch the wild rabbits with ease.

Barney was always on duty warning us of the arrival of strangers. She slept out of doors in a snug kennel and never failed to accompany us on night duties, regardless of weather conditions.

Barney suffered from delusions of grandeur and on occasions she treated the other dogs with utter disdain. She would totally ignore them for days on end, except on occasions when she went broody and tried to mother them and carry them by the scruff of the neck. Like an old she-elephant Barney was definitely the matriarch. She wasn't a greedy dog – she delicately selected the pick of the titbits, leaving most of the rest for her canine pals. She passed away at a ripe old age. Like all the other dogs she was sadly missed not only by us, her workmates, but by members of the public that knew her well.

Rosie, alias Houdini, was one of the neighbours' dogs who was extremely lovable and very boisterous – everyone's friend. A large Old English Sheepdog pup, she loved everyone and given the opportunity she would lick them to death. Rosie arrived as a tiny pup but grew at an extraordinary rate until she towered over the other two dogs. Despite the efforts of her owners she could escape from the most secure places. When a ship blew for the lock there was no way she would miss out on the bones and titbits. She would appear as if by magic. Unfortunately she wasn't with us very long. Finally her owners could not cope with her escaping ability and gave her to a farmer. She now has the run of many acres but I reckon she misses the thrill of the bones.

'Arry lived in a company canalside cottage with his very thin but equally peculiar wife Cissie. Along with them resided several ducks, hens, a goat, innumerable cats and a blind dog.

Once 'Arry allegedly had the stature of a whippet when he worked locks and walked for miles leading the boat horse. One of the older employees verified this fact when a baggin debate focused on body weight, diet and fitness. These morning altercations usually took place in a crowded smelly boat cabin or lock hut. The discussions touched on every subject under the sun. Of course during the debate at least one of the lads identified himself as an expert on the matter in hand. The near-arguments were usually triggered by an item allegedly read by one of the men in the Sunday papers. Incidentally it was usually a paper no one else had read, which had been unfortunately thrown away or left at home.

Since coming ashore to live and work 'Arry had spectacularly gone to seed, hence the debate on fatness and fitness on this occasion. According to him he had just developed a land man's figure.

Enforced idleness and a continuous diet of fried greasy food liberally washed down with gallons of beer did not help his once sylphlike shape.

The vast amounts of ale he consumed were usually paid for in the summer boating season by gullible holidaymakers when they moored their pleasure boats overnight alongside the towpath by 'Arry's local pub. Winter was a bleak time for 'Arry but he had another trick up his sleeve to carry him partially through the bad times. On balmy summer evenings and weekends he took up station at a pair of staircase locks located by his cottage. Hire boat holidaymakers, unsure of how they could negotiate the formidable obstacle, turned to 'Arry for help.

His reward, a couple of bottles of beer donated by the grateful amateur boaties, was traded with the manager of his local pub for his favourite tipple, Guinness.

'Arry considered the gallons of beer he wheedled out of the tourists to be a form of a professional fee they paid in return for the outlandish stories when he related them. These were usually lurid and greatly exaggerated tales of his days on the cut as a professional boatie.

"You see, lads," he explained. "I've got no schooling. Them silly sods that come into the pub playing at boaties 'ave the edification. Yet..!"

At this point 'Arry paused until he gained complete attention. "...who is it amongst the boozers that gets all the free drinks then?" There was no answer to that argument.

This unaccustomed idle lifestyle ashore had definitely taken its toll on 'Arry's body.

Regardless of weather, come summer, come winter he wore his company-supplied steel toe-capped Wellingtons. His short body was permanently encased in bib and brace overalls straining at the seams. On a rare occasion I saw 'Arry with his donkey jacket off. At his rear his wife had sewn a broad expansion gusset made of some kind of elastic material.

"Saves buying new gear as I grow a bit," he explained proudly. "This is my idea. Good, eh? I've got to watch the old pennies."

'Arry was never seen spending a penny. Rumours were he was very rich despite his appearance. His protruding belly, always about nine inches ahead of him, was supported by a thick leather belt studded with Army badges and an enormous brass buckle, made by himself, he proudly boasted. It was fashioned from the remnants of his last boat-horse's harness.

So much depended on the belt and buckle; everyone believed it held 'Arry together, as he was never seen without it. One of his mates joked, when the belt appeared to be violin-string tight after a particularly long session on the beer followed by a huge meal of double portions of fish and chips, "Have you had that belt checked out lately, 'Arry? You should get the lads from the repair yard to give it an annual test. Bit like an MOT, eh, 'Arry?"

Another joined in, contributing, "If that thing gives way we better look out, your guts will be spread for miles around, wiping out half the village."

They received an immediate response from the unruffled recipient of his warped sense of humour.

"It's you skinny sods that better watch out. Everyone knows you lot die of consumption before you're fifty."

One of his tormentors skulked off, muttering, "You shouldn't talk about disease like that. It's not funny. Me granddad died of TB."

'Arry gave the V sign to his mate's disappearing back, a victorious grin adorning his dirty face.

His overalls were a source of wonderment to us. The area below the chin and above the belt shone as if made of oilskin. Where the grease and food-stained fabric rested on the bar of his favourite lock-side pub there was a definite line, indicating its height.

'Arry was one of those men that could sustain four days' growth of beard endlessly on his weather-beaten face. His head was inevitably crammed into a greasy, once-checked cap, with a broken peak and split seam at the back. It was rumoured his head was completely bald beneath its greasy mantle, but nobody could verify this.

Neither 'Arry nor his wife had a tooth in their heads. This deficiency was entirely due to them consuming part of the cargo of sweet chocolate they delivered to the Midlands in their boating days. They had however inherited his father's false teeth which they shared on occasions. The old man for some reason on his deathbed had insisted on leaving his belongings shared equally between 'Arry and Cissie. They had interpreted his wishes literally.

One of his fellow workers told me the following story, swearing it was true. He went to call for 'Arry to help him sort out an emergency on the canal. The problem arose in the early hours of the morning. When he knocked on the cottage door a cacophony of noise greeted him.

The dog howled, the hens squawked and the goat bleated – all from within the house. 'Arry responded to the animal noises and the continuous knocking on the front door by opening the upstairs window and sending forth a welter of blistering curses.

His head was as usual adorned in the greasy cap. His upper body that could be seen in the torch's beam was clothed in the inevitable overalls. When 'Arry realised there was overtime in the offing he was out of the front door in a flash, his feet already shod in his steel toe-capped Wellies.

In the early eighties the company began issuing donkey jackets to the workers. 'Arry complained on the second annual issue that his previous coat was too big. After much argument with the issuing clerk, he allowed 'Arry to choose from the stores one that was obviously too small but suited 'Arry, although he wouldn't try the coat on in the clerk's presence. After another prolonged squabble for the sake of peace and quiet the clerk gave up and let him go on his way.

The next time 'Arry was observed scurrying to the pub with his wife she was proudly togged out in the new donkey jacket with the company logo blacked out on her back.

It must be admitted, 'Arry was talented in many ways. He certainly could live off the land, be it in a city or the country. He could handle boats with natural ease while plotting and planning his next deal. He certainly had a gift with animals, especially horses and dogs. As an unofficial vet he treated many of his mates' animals successfully. But one of his more scary achievements was as a medic advising and treating some of his mates and their families. Many of the ex-boaties swore by his skill as a healer and bone-setter.

When I questioned him about this gift, he explained his father and grandfather had had the same skill before him. When they lived and worked the boats, doctors were few and far between and could not be afforded anyway. Cuts, headaches, coughs, colds – he had remedies for all of them. Broken limbs had also been treated in the past.

One of the lads, Sam, was prone to boils on his neck. He was terrified of doctors, and despite our urging he refused to go to the local surgery. Sam was a strange lad. Even though he had been through the education system it seemed to have passed him by. Like most of the boaties he could not read or write. To describe Sam accurately, he was two pence short of a bob. 'Arry seemed to have taken him under his wing since he started work on the cut. This particular morning 'Arry spotted yet another huge carbuncle on his neck and offered to treat it for him. He was rewarded with a prompt refusal from the possible patient. As the day moved on the poor lad must have been suffering badly, and at dinner time he relented and agreed to 'Arry treating his affliction. 'Arry instructed him to lie face down on the bench, close his eyes and relax. From his bag full of all kinds of weird things he used for treating his victims, 'Arry extracted an empty meat paste jar. He heated it by filling it with boiling water from the kettle on the stove. We could see the lad was terrified and we assured him 'Arry knew what he was doing. I advised him to close his eyes as instructed and take it easy, 'Arry would put him right. After a while the apparatus was evidently ready to 'Arry's satisfaction. Using a boilermaker's leather glove he removed the heated jar from the stove. We watched with fascination as he placed it with the open neck over the offending boil. When the heated bottle touched his neck, Sam leapt to his feet with a scream of pain, and swearing like a trooper he rushed out of the door with the jar firmly attached to his neck by vacuum. 'Arry nodded with satisfaction and advised us this was a usual reaction to the treatment, when we showed our alarm at this startling turn of events.

"We shall have to catch him though and get that jar off his neck, otherwise it will suck his brains out," he added with conviction.

It took six of us to eventually corner poor Sam, but every time we tried to approach him to remove the jar he threatened us with a slancing hook. He had his back to a picket fence swinging the hook in wide circles, confounding our efforts to help him. From my position I saw 'Arry furtively approaching from the other side of the fence carrying a sweeping brush. He arrived within striking distance of the raging Sam, undetected. With an accurately aimed blow he swept the pus-filled jar off Sam's neck. The lad let out an almighty roar and promptly fainted. 'Arry came through the gate, examined Sam's neck, and nodded with satisfaction at a job well done. He poured a blue packet of salt from a crisp packet on his patient's neck and wandered away whistling. Sam recovered from his faint, staggered to his feet and tottered off to the lock hut for a lie down at my insistence. Another satisfied customer for one of 'Arry's rough and ready remedies.

I assumed that after this crude treatment Sam would never consult 'Arry on medical matters again, but I was proved wrong.

Monday morning baggin time witnessed a gathering of the lads after yet another weekend off work. I couldn't quite figure what Sam and 'Arry had been whispering about on Friday as when I approached them, they furtively ceased conversing.

"Those buggers are up to something," Brickie warned us. "They have been at it all day. Mark my words, there is a deal or something going on and the sods don't want to share it with us."

"Miserable tight arses, they can whistle in future if I get on to something good," Puddler, who had never got onto anything good in his life, vowed. They eventually went home at the end of the day and we were still none the wiser what the plotting pair were up to.

The next day Sam entered the hut first but would not disclose any details of the deal he had with 'Arry, despite intense questioning and even veiled threats. 'Arry strolled in later after he had retrieved the unfortunate victims from his snares. Not a word was spoken between them. 'Arry nodded at Sam. Sam gave 'Arry the thumbs up sign. This went on every morning for about a week and still we couldn't get a clue what the pair were up to.

The weekend came and went. On Monday morning 'Arry arrived but no Sam. 'Arry looked slightly concerned and replied, when he was asked were his mate was, "Should be 'ere, I'm not his bleedin' dad." (Although the resemblance of the two characters led some of the lads to suspect something had occurred between Sam's widowed mother and 'Arry many years ago.) "Saw him Saturday in the boozer, seemed all right then."

When we tried to press him he responded with, "Got a bit of business on, be back shortly. If anyone asks, someone has reported a cow in the river, an' I've gone to get it out."

This was the usual cover story the lads used to explain unofficial absences off the job.

Pontius Pilot the foreman arrived looking all of a dither. He proudly answered to the nickname of 'The Pilot'. The poor bugger thought the name complimented his ability with a narrowboat, his hobby. He donned a Captain's cap of a weekend, cruising the waterways while shouting a string of conflicting orders at his brow-beaten wife. The truth was that his nickname was related to an unfortunate expression he frequently used when the going got tough: "I wash my hands of these sods."

"Where's 'Arry?" was his first question.

"Cow in the river, a walker reported it. 'Arry's gone to sort it out, he shouldn't be long."

I was left to make the excuses to the foreman – the rest of the lads had scattered and looked busy when the lookout reported his van approaching. He gave me an old-fashioned look. He had heard this excuse many times but had never actually seen a cow in the river during his long career on the cut.

I tried a little bit of psychological sympathy, an old tactic Pontius usually fell for.

"What's up?" I enquired. "You look absolutely knackered. Here, sit yourself down and I'll make you a brew."

He slumped onto the bench and unloaded his woe on me.

"Bloody hell, I've had a right night. I don't know! I feel like a bloody nursemaid to this lot. I got this phone call from the police just after midnight.

"I had just got into bed after being called out for another problem. You know what it's like – don't get a minute to myself..." Pontius continued whinging. He got no sympathy from me on that one. All the lads suspected he generated these call-outs to give himself overtime. We observed he always got called out coincidentally when a flat week's pay was looming.

"Kids again, I suppose?" I found myself tutting ever so sympathetically.

"You could say it was 'kids', it was that silly bugger, Sam. Would you believe the silly sod was dancing bollock-naked in his garden in the moonlight? The only thing he had on was one of those Walkman things, you know – that play tapes. Do you know what tape he was playing when the cops caught him?"

I shrugged and told him, "I have no idea."

"*Zorba the Greek!* Zorba the bloody Greek! I ask you?"

That triggered something in my mind. I retorted, "Oh Yes! Paul saw the picture not long ago. He has got this thing about wanting to go to Crete for a holiday. He wants to be able to do the Greek dancing before he goes there. I suppose he was only practising, poor bugger."

"Ah, but without a stitch on? I know it's hot in Greece but do they allow nudes to prance about? I wash my hands of this lot, I really do.

"You know his garden backs onto that lock on the cut? Well evidently the people of the pleasure boats were on their way back to the boats after a night out when they spotted the silly sod. They only rang the cops and complained – they thought he was an escaped nutter from that cuckoo farm up the road. Bloody idiot! I told the cops when they rang me it was nothing to do with me but they rang the boss. He reckoned that because it's a company house, and Sam and his mother live in it, it was our problem. Anyway, when I got there they had already arrested him for indecent exposure. His old mother went mad when I knocked her up. She thought the silly bugger was in bed fast asleep. I had to take her and some of Sam's clothes, down to the cop shop. Fancy the cops taking him away starkers – I mean he was in his own garden, after all."

I commiserated, trying to stifle my laughter.

"You would think you were allowed to do what you liked in your own garden!"

Pontius nodded in agreement and continued moaning.

"Boy, was she giving me earache on the way. You would think it was all my bloody fault. Talk about shooting the messenger? Hey! Have you ever met his mother?"

Before I could answer he began describing her. "She's got a bloody moustache – you know, it's better than my old fella's. That wart on her nose doesn't help either. You would think with all the medical advances she would have that burnt off. Eh! I reckon in years gone by they would have burnt her as a witch."

His voice dropped to a whisper and he looked furtively around to see if he was being overheard. "Do you reckon that lad Sam looks like 'Arry?

On the alert for a trap, I kept my opinion to myself. He shuddered. "I've heard it said 'Arry was giving her one years ago when he was on the trade boats. I don't know how even 'Arry could fancy her. Jeez she is as rough as a bear's arse. What do you reckon?"

"Stranger things happen at sea, you know!" I replied. What a stupid thing to say, but I had to respond negatively. I knew Pontius of old. If I'd gone along with the rumour about 'Arry and Sam's mother having it off, some time in the future he would have credited me with starting it. He gave me a strange look and slumped in the corner, sipping his tea.

I had to know more but I knew he would take his time and drag the story out to get the maximum sympathy. I credited myself with being able to extract goodies from guys like Pontius. I felt a bit like a father confessor sometimes. I must have the kind of face that makes them trust me.

'Arry arrived back at the lock.

"Well, did you get the cow out?" Pontius asked him.

'Arry looked a bit puzzled. After a small pause he answered vaguely, "I couldn't find the bugger. Must have got out itself, I reckon."

"Right then, 'Arry! Now that the tale of the cow is out of the way, what's all this about Sam? What kind of crap have you been feeding the daft bugger? I've had a right night with him, his old woman, and the cops. He hasn't said as much but I feel your influence is somehow involved."

Unusually for 'Arry, he sat down and admitted responsibility for the lad's actions.

"He suffers with Rhumatiz you see?" he explained. "Been to all kind of doctors and quacks but nothing cured him. He's been taking pills and medicine for years. Anyway his old lady asked me to help, being as I'm noted as a bit of a medicine man."

He asked me proudly, "You know that, don't you?" I had to agree he had accomplished some amazing cures on cases medical science had given up as lost causes.

"Well, anyway, I don't usually treat Rhumatiz but the lad was desperate. I suggested a very old remedy my granddad used to cure people."

I could see Pontius was getting bored with the whole episode as he continually looked at his watch.

"Get on with it, 'Arry, for God's sake. I've other things to do except sitting here listening to all your crap. What did you tell Sam to do that got him in trouble with the law?"

'Arry confessed, "I told him to find a place where there are plenty of nettles. It had to be the week when the moon is full, a couple of nights before and after. He was to strip off, rub himself down with dock leaves and run back and to through the nettles."

Pontius looked amazed. "And he did that? The silly bugger!"

'Arry protested, "It was bloody working, I tell you. He's been doing it for a week now and he reckons his Rhumatiz has nearly gone. You've seen him giving me the thumbs-up all week?"

'Arry appealed to me again, and I had to agree.

He continued, "I didn't know the silly bugger was letting his garden grow wild and taking the treatment in full view of the cut. I thought he was going up to the woods over yonder."

Pontius leapt up.

"I've bloody heard everything now. I wouldn't like to be in your shoes when his old woman finds out it was all down to you, 'Arry. She'll stop your tap all right."

He was still giggling as he left the hut and jumped in his van.

"What's he on about stopping me tap, the silly sod?" 'Arry complained. I refrained from enlightening him.

I suffered with Rhumatiz myself but despite the obvious improvement in Sam's condition – and it was noticeable when the lad returned to work – I could not bring myself to partake in 'Arry's drastic remedy.

Poor Sam was bound over by the magistrate to keep the peace and refrain from exposing himself in public. Not once did he implicate 'Arry, but the lads noticed that Sam's house was given a wide berth by 'Arry from then on.

The first time I saw Sam when he returned to work, he asked, "Can I have a word with you, Scouse, on my own, like?" I agreed and we stood by the lock side when he divulged his problem.

"You know when I had to go before them magistrate fellas? You know what? I think I am going to get the sack. I don't want to lose this job, Scouse. I didn't mean no harm."

Alarmed because this was the first I had heard about it, I enquired. "Who is going to sack you? I don't think so. If you are to be given the push I think I would have been notified by the Personnel Manager."

I liked to think I had a good working relationship with the personnel department.

Sam answered miserably, "It's something the magistrate fella said. I've known him since I was a kid. I thought 'cos he knew me and my mum it would be all right. My mum used to clean his house for him and she took me around there, he was always kind to me then."

He didn't explain the details until I urged him on.

"Out with it Sam, what did he say?"

At last Sam explained.

"Well, he said something really weird, but get this, Scouse, he kind of laughed when he said it. I thought nothing of it at the time but my mother told me he was going to get me the sack. She is really pissed off with me 'cos I got copped in the nude."

Sam changed tack and asked me a seemingly unrelated question.

"Scouse! How long have I been a whippersnapper? I thought I was just an ordinary canal man?"

Sam's query baffled me. I had many of these conversations with him and I always came away from the encounters in a kind of mental fog.

I like to believe I am very tolerant but I found myself losing patience on this occasion. Sam had a habit of making me do that. I sternly ordered him, "Right Sam, no more around the houses. Just tell me what he said. I don't want to hear what your mother said. No more questions, just give me the facts."

At last I got to what was worrying Sam when he revealed: "The magistrate said, 'This kind of behaviour will not be tolerated in a civilised society. No doubt your employers will hear of your escapade. You are no longer a young whippersnapper, you cannot expose your falderals and gewgaws in public. I hope you learn by your mistakes, so let this be the end of it.'"

Poor Sam he looked so serious. Despite the urge to I didn't laugh, I assured him his job was safe – the magistrate was only doing what a magistrate does.

It's a long time since I heard expressions like those used myself and that was on a TV programme. I decided the man must be a quiz or crossword freak.

Something came out of Sam's encounter with the judiciary.

When he told the lads about his brush with the magistrate from then on he acquired another couple of nicknames.

Chapter Three
The arch enemy

A COUPLE OF the lads related the following story. Much to my regret, I did not witness the beginning of the escapade but I did however observe 'Arry arriving at the cabin soaked to the skin and his subsequent defeat in a deal by his old enemy, the farmer known as Grabber.

It appears 'Arry was doing his morning mooch along the canal, sniffing here, poking there, collecting the overnight victims of his snares. He spotted an adversary, namely a farmer, lying on the narrowest part of the towpath trying to persuade a cow to come ashore. The cow was up to its shoulders in the middle of the canal. Attached to the beast by a long piece of rope looped over the cow's horns was the farmer.

Seeing the opportunity to make a few bob and maybe score a few points off his enemy, 'Arry approached the scene. His two workmates, part of the canal gang carrying out grass cutting on the towpath, sat back on the boat cabin roof to enjoy the entertainment while having their baggin.

A local man walking his dog arrived and asked the lads on the work boat, "What's happening?"

One of them replied, "Hang about mate, you're witnessing a battle of the giants here. Two of the local villains will be trying to out-fox each other."

"It's not 'Arry is it?" the man asked, a touch of awe reflected in his voice.

"Yes, and that mean sod of a farmer, Grabber from over there," the lad replied, indicating the nearby farmhouse.

"Good, this should be fun. I haven't witnessed one of Arry's skirmishes first hand since that business with the pet shop's parrot. Mind if I hang about to watch?"

The lad shrugged, "Please yourself pal, but you will have to tell me about the parrot show. I haven't heard about this before."

The dog walker settled down on a milestone to rubberneck the confrontation and replied with a slight impatience in his tone, "Later, I'll tell you about the parrot later. I don't want to miss a second of this one."

'Arry's reputation amongst those that frequented the cut was legendary in these parts.

The farmer, on recognising 'Arry as a canal authority, expressed joy. "Thank goodness you've come."

"What's up, pal?" 'Arry asked the obvious question.

The farmer replied in a sneering manner, "What do you think? I was giving the cow her weekly bath and she won't come out. Naughty girl, isn't she, eh?" Under his breath he muttered, "Bloody pillock!"

'Arry was game for a bit of piss-taking at the expense of Farmer Grabber. This was the very same person that had thwarted his efforts to pillage his consumable crops on a few occasions.

'Arry replied thoughtfully, "Not sure, me old mate, but I think it's against regulations for cows to take baths in the canal. I shall have to report this to my foreman. You might need a licence, you see?"

'Arry began to stroll away but the farmer desperately called him back.

"Don't be daft, 'Arry, I've been stuck here for a couple of hours. I daren't let the sod go or she will be off like a shot to the other side. I'll have a hell of a job getting her back if she gets over there. You know what a narky bugger Old Bill will be if she gets to his prize bull. He's still going on about the last time it happened two years ago."

'Arry asked, "I thought those fields were yours over the bridge?"

"They are except that one over there. I rent it out to that miserable sod Bill. Sorry I did, he's nowt but trouble, always moaning about something or other," the Grabber replied impatiently, trying to keep the anger out of his voice.

"I bet you get a few bob, though, eh?" 'Arry enquired.

"Bloody hell, 'Arry, that's the last thing on my mind. See, I just managed to lasso the bugger, practically got her ashore until she gave a tug and very nearly pulled the rope off me. The bloody thing is too short to be of any good. Look..." he revealed the very end of the rope in his hand.

"Fancies that bull over there, then, does she? That cow of yours?" 'Arry asked, indicating the huge bull in the field on the opposite side.

"What a stupid question – are you going to help me or what?" Grabber replied angrily. His voice changed as he pleaded in a cajoling tone, "Arry, come on, mate, please. I'm bursting for a crap – do something, will you?"

"Well, there's not a lot I can do. Hmmm!" 'Arry scratched his head under his cap. "Cow's a big bugger, isn't she? Bet she's a heavy sod? Eh! What time is it?"

Grabber looked at his watch with difficulty, told him the time, then asked, "What you bloody worrying about the time for? That's the last thing you should be mithering me about."

'Arry joyfully added to the farmer's problems.

"Boats will start coming along shortly," he observed. "It's going to be chaos here in a while. You know the hire boats have got to be back at the base at twelve o'clock today. If they're late the companies will bung you the bill, you know!"

Grabber was getting frantic. The idea of paying compensation appalled him. This particular farmer was a noted miser or 'tight-arse' as 'Arry called him. 'Arry rubbed his chin thoughtfully as he explored possible solutions.

"I could ring the office and get them to send a crane."

The farmer's expression changed to one of relief as he saw the possibility of release from his predicament. 'Arry deflated him, "But that'll cost you a fortune and I know you won't want to spend money, will yeah? You being a bit of a tight-arse. You are, ain't you?"

'Arry added thoughtfully, "Anyway we wouldn't be able to get a crane along. Towpath's too narrow, you see? I reckon we could get the crane to that bridge back yonder though. But would it take the weight, I ask myself?"

This suggestion further infuriated the farmer. "Course, it would take the weight, you silly sod. I use it all the time to get to my fields over the cut."

'Arry offered another solution. "If that rope was longer you could tie it to that tree over there. But it's too short isn't it?"

The farmer glared at his enemy but conceded, as 'Arry was his only hope. He restrained his anger and addressed his adversary in a persuasive manner. Grabber desperately tried another tack, bribery.

"'Arry if you hold this rope for me while I organise something myself, I'll give you a pound."

"A pound, you say, for just holding that there rope? Hmmm! Eh, but? I'd have to lie down where you are, wouldn't I, being the rope's so short? Phew! Don't fancy that, matey. Grass is damp, got Rhumatiz, you see?"

"A fiver, and that's my lot," the farmer offered recklessly, upping the reward.

'Arry saw his chance and moved in quickly for the kill.

"Make it a tenner, and you've got a deal."

The farmer groaned and agreed to 'Arry's extortionate demand. He offered the end of the rope to 'Arry. 'Arry stepped back a pace. "Let's see the colour of your money first," 'Arry insisted.

"Bloody hell! Don't you trust me? I'll square you up later. You don't think I carry that much money on me, do you?" Grabber replied and explained in a whisper that his need to go to the toilet was paramount. 'Arry grinned as he commiserated with the pleading farmer.

"Need a tom tit; desperate are you, eh?"

'Arry went into thinking mode. "Tell you what! Give me your watch, you know, as a sign of good faith, I'll give it back when you turn up with the tenner, honest."

The farmer rashly agreed. Holding the end of the rope in his teeth he undid the wrist watch and handed it and the end of the rope to 'Arry as he took up position alongside him. The farmer climbed to his feet and farted loudly. He swore as he followed through and raced towards the farmhouse, leaving a foul smell behind him.

Two fishermen turned up, sniffed the air, grimaced, and stood observing 'Arry for a minute before one of them inquired, "Going to be lying there long, mate?"

'Arry gave him a withering look without answering. The fisherman continued, explaining, "You see, we've got a fishing match along here today and you are lying in our peg mark spot."

'Arry replied, "Tell you what, mate! See that boat over there with them two grinning sods lazin' about on it? Do us a favour, mate. Nip along and ask them to bring me a good length of line, will you?"

One of the fishermen dropped his basket and gear and walked along towards the boat. His mate sat on his basket and began to assemble his rod. The other fisherman was back in a minute empty-handed.

"Where's the line, then?" 'Arry enquired.

"Them fellas asked, what do you want it for?"

"Bloody idiots, wait until I've sorted this stupid cow out and I'll sort them two sods out, too! Tell 'em it's to tie to the bloody cow."

Off went the fisherman, this time joined by his mate. He asked 'Arry as he moved away. "Will you keep an eye on our gear, mate, seeing as you're hangin' about, so to speak?" The two men moved towards the boat laughing.

Two ladies on horses arrived. They stopped by 'Arry and asked him to move as he was blocking the towpath.

The fishermen returned empty-handed.

"Where's the line, then?" 'Arry asked. Before the fishermen had time to reply one horse lady interceded, "Are you going to move and let us pass?"

She dismounted and impatiently prodded 'Arry with her shiny riding boot.

"Come on, you lazy sod, move your fat backside and let us pass. This towpath is for horses, not for lazing about sleeping off your drunken orgies or playing cowboys."

'Arry moaned, "Bloody hell, Missus. I should be so lucky to

afford a drunken orgy. Can't you see? I'm stuck here holdin' on to this bloody animal, and stop bloody kicking me, will you. It hurts, you vicious cow!"

Angrily she replied while giving 'Arry another shove with her boot, "I'm not kicking you, you foul-mouthed lout. If I so chose to kick you, you would feel it, I can tell you. Haw, haw."

Her companion interceded proudly, "She's got a mighty kick, I'll have you know, haven't you Felicity? Played for the college soccer team don't you know? Haw, haw."

'Arry, evidently not winning the exchange and fearing the lady would do as she threatened, addressed the fishermen, "Where's the line then?"

Sniggering, the fisherman replied, "Them mates of yours said, what cow are you on about?"

'Arry sent forth a stream of profanities in their direction

The local Probus rambling club, consisting of about twenty elderly walkers, arrived. Their leader asked 'Arry. "What are you doing, my man?"

'Arry, just about to explode and give him a mouthful, recognised some of the ramblers as retired Waterways managers. He realised he had to be diplomatic in case they reported him. Patiently he explained he was saving the cow from drowning.

"That is very commendable, good man."

The leader turned to his companions. "This is what I have been telling you. This man is the salt of the earth. He may be ugly and a rather dirty-looking fellow, but when the chips are down this is the man for me."

He turned to 'Arry again and made an offer to assist. "Why don't we give you a hand, chappie? Maybe if all of us pull on the rope, we can get the cow out of the canal?"

'Arry showed him the short end with an eye spliced into it.

"Not long enough, the rope, you see, Mister. Thanks for the offer, though. The farmer has gone for help, anyway. It shouldn't be long now."

The ramblers photographed the scene, then carefully stepping over 'Arry's prone body, they squeezed passed the horses and continued on their walk. The other horse lady dismounted, muttering complaints. The pair of horsy ladies stood impatiently by their nervous mounts.

'Arry had an idea. He carefully undid his thick leather belt from around his waist, slipped the end through the eye of the rope and re-buckled his belt. Carefully straining on the rope with his considerable weight, and bracing his feet on the pile tops, he achieved an upright sitting position. The horse ladies prepared to get on their restless mounts.

"It's about time, too," one remarked to her companion.

She replied, "Bloody fool's lazing about in our way, with no thought for others. We'll be late for elevenses at this rate."

'Arry leaned back, grasped the rope in both hands and strenuously heaved himself to his feet. The bewildered cow, with its head twisted in an awkward angle towards the straining 'Arry, let out a bellow of pain.

Perhaps it was the sight of 'Arry's unusual shape, accompanied by his grunts and groans, plus his roar of triumph. Maybe it was the bellow of the tortured cow that triggered the next calamity, the lads are not sure. Nevertheless, one of the horses reared, snatched the rein out of its owner's hand and bolted down the towpath scattering the fishermen and their gear.

'Arry grimly hung on to the cow.

The horseless lady cursed 'Arry and raced after her galloping runaway. She was followed by her companion after she delivered 'Arry a good thwack on his backside with her riding crop. 'Arry startled, eased up on the cow. She gave him a pull and he tottered but managed to recover on the very edge of the cut. The onlookers gasped. 'Arry, with a look of victory adorning his face, pulled his tongue at his mates. The fishermen cursed everyone and surveyed their mangled gear. Another batch of anglers arrived for the match.

The roar of a heavy engine approaching at speed was heard. 'Arry began to win the battle with the cow and actually dragged it towards him, until the sound of the engine was joined by a screech. A fire engine arrived at the bridge with its siren wailing. The cow, already frightened, retaliated and made a dash away from the deafening noise with 'Arry in tow.

The lads spotted the foreman approaching. They jumped off the cabin and pretended to be sorting out their grass strimmers. Pontius enquired, "What's going on here, then? Where's that idle bugger, 'Arry?"

The foreman, a look of amazement on his face, spotted 'Arry disappearing and reappearing in huge eruptions of water as the terrified cow dragged him up the canal.

The man with the dog informed him gleefully, "'Arry is demonstrating water skiing to the fishermen and fire brigade. What a star."

Eventually, the cow and 'Arry were rescued by the fire brigade two fields down the cut. 'Arry was not looking too bad considering the ordeal he had just been through. Certainly, he was a great deal cleaner than he had been for years, as the lads hilariously pointed out to him later.

The fishing match went ahead after the club secretary complained to the foreman, "It's not right allowing cows and people to mess around in the canal. Upsets the fish, you know? You buggers charge enough for licences, it's the least you could do is keep them out on match days."

Despite bursting into uncontrollable laughter at times, the lads cut the grass without the able assistance of their mate.

The dog man, dragging his unfortunate pooch behind, hurried to his local pub to tell his boozing cronies another chapter in the 'Arry saga.

The secretary of the Probus ramblers wrote to the canal manager commending 'Arry for his dedication to work and for saving the cow.

The RSPCA heard about his exploits and wanted to present 'Arry with a humane award.

As for the horse ladies, we heard one of them got herself fined for allowing her horse to be unattended on the highway. We were informed from a very reliable source she is currently searching for 'Arry with vengeance in mind, armed with a riding crop.

'Arry? Well he arrived at the lock cabin to dry out very dejected, delivered in the back of the foreman's pick-up. Pontius refused to allow him into the cab because of his wet condition. To make matters worse, when I contacted Grabber on the phone at 'Arry's insistence, regarding the ten pounds he owed, the farmer refused to pay and directed me to tell poor 'Arry so. Quote: "Tell him there is no way I'm giving that scrounging sod ten pounds. What he can do is keep the watch and shove it up his anal orifice. The bloody thing is no good anyway after being in the water. Ha. You can tell him this as well, ha, ha and this will really piss him off. I got the watch free from the garage with my diesel oil."

He added with relish, "I also have another seven in my house if 'Arry wants to buy them at ten pounds each."

'Arry and I could clearly hear him cackling with glee over the phone.

This was not one of 'Arry's better days and he swore revenge on his enemy.

One consolation that pleased 'Arry no end, was that we heard a week later that the Fire Brigade had sent the farmer a bill for their services in rescuing the love-sick cow.

It took a while for 'Arry to dream up a scheme to avenge his injured pride. The lads were working by a bridge site in a vandal-prone area. The council was strengthening the bridge and our lads kept the towpath and cut clear of debris. Monday morning when they turned to, they spent the first hour or so clearing up after the kids' weekend fun. Notice boards indicating a weak bridge seemed to be a favourite target for the vandals and had to be fished out of the cut. Luckily they floated down to the nearest lock and were easily retrievable. As the lads recovered them one Monday, 'Arry, being unable to read, asked them why the notice boards were so important. When they explained the role of the notices one of the lads reckoned he saw a gleam in 'Arry's eyes.

Another Monday came, and the council men asked the lads to retrieve the boards. However, they were not in the usual site when they searched and new ones had to be ordered. It was about six weeks later that the boards turned up. The section inspector had a complaining phone call from Farmer Grabber, asking how long it would be until the bridge repairs were complete, and when he could use the crossing again. It seemed, when the foreman investigated his complaint, that the bridge he used to get across the cut to his fields had been closed for six weeks. Official notices were posted at either end indicating it was a weak bridge. It meant him doing a long detour with his machinery, incurring much delay and expense. The notices puzzled the foreman as they were not the ones utilised by his company. He explained to the farmer that it was most probably the council that had posted the warning notices.

"Have you been running heavy machines over here? These bridges are old, you know, maybe you have buggered it up."

One of the lads, 'Arry's mate who accompanied the foreman, added his pennyworth.

"Shouldn't be surprised if the council don't send you a bill for repairs. One of the farmers down the cut got hit for thousands off the council for some repairs they did to the bridge he was using."

All the lads knew Grabber ran his tractors and machinery over the bridge. The farmer blanched, made his excuses and left in a hurry. 'Arry's mate related the story to us when he returned, much to the old villain's delight who wanted every detail of the occurrence. We never found out if 'Arry had posted the warning boards, but he certainly enjoyed the sight of his enemy using the long detour to his fields every time he worked in that area.

Some days I thought I must be going soft in the head. I had a day's holiday clear of the usual dramas and traumas of the cut. I had been invited to speak at a local women's group meeting about my world travels on the Churchill Fellowship. This meant no getting up early and a leisurely drive to a picturesque village out in the country. Whistling to myself, I was driving carefree along through the lanes when I spotted 'Arry, standing at a bus stop with a parcel under his arm. Should I? Or shouldn't I? That was the question. I knew he was totally dependent on buses or lifts to get anywhere from his remote house to the nearest shops. Neither 'Arry nor his wife was able to drive. Against my better judgement I pulled to a stop alongside him. Without being invited, he squeezed himself into the passenger seat with an "All right, pal?" greeting.

"Where are you off to then, 'Arry?" I enquired. "Not on the cut today, I see?"

It was an obvious observation but this was how close proximity to 'Arry puddled my brain.

"Nah!" he informed me. "I've got a bit of business on at the village. I heard you were coming past here this morning."

"Oh!" I answered sarcastically. "Lucky for you I'm going in that direction, then. I'll drop you off on the way through, shall I?"

"Aye, that'll do," he replied.

How he always knew my business amazed me. He had a better intelligence service than the government, and never missed a trick to save a few bob. This morning he would save a few pence on bus fare.

I began putting the car in gear when I noticed 'Arry hadn't applied his seat belt.

"'Arry, put your seat belt on, please," I instructed him.

"Don't believe in the buggers," he declined my instruction to fit it.

I pointed out, "I can't drive until you put it on, mate. It's my insurance and licence at risk, you see?"

"Stupid bloody things," he moaned and tried pulling the strap over his enormous belly. There was no way it would reach the anchoring point. I got out of the car and went around to his side, opened the door and attempted to fit his seat belt. No matter how I tried, extending it and hauling it with all my might it would not fit. I tried adjusting the seat as far backward as possible, still no joy. I stood back and scratched my head.

"It looks like they weren't designed for someone with your proportions, 'Arry," I complained.

He smirked in triumph. "I told you they were bloody useless. Tell you what, rather than arse around all day I'll stretch the bugger over me belly and pretend it's fastened, will that do you?"

There was nothing else to do except permit this traffic infringement. I suppose I could have ejected him from the car, but then what? I returned to the driving seat defeated yet again by the old scoundrel and set off.

"What time are you coming back, then?" he enquired.

There was no way I was tying myself to one of 'Arry's days out, chauffeuring him about. One of the drivers had warned me about the time he offered him a lift and was stuck with him and Cissie all day.

"Oh, I don't know, could be all day. Might even come back another way. It's my day off, you see," I responded warily.

'Arry grunted disapprovingly. "You're a lucky bugger having a car. Me and my Missus couldn't afford one on the money those tight buggers pay us."

I gave a snort of disbelief. I knew, as everyone else knew on the cut, that 'Arry could buy and sell the lot of us just through his unofficial trading and activities, discounting his wages. He gave me one of his nudges with the elbow and grimaced a self-satisfied smirk

I had seen that same look on other rich people when they disclosed annually the three richest people in Britain on the television. I shuddered with the thought of one day seeing 'Arry being paraded on the media. A thought passed through my mind – if and when it did happen, would 'Arry still be dressed in the same gear? I smiled to myself as I visualised the scene and the shock on the viewers' faces.

We arrived at the village. I dropped 'Arry off where he indicated, thankful for escaping so easily, and hurriedly drove away in case he had other plans for me.

I had a nice time with the village ladies, showed my slides, drank buckets of tea from delicate china cups and ate hundredweights of homemade cake. I tactfully judged one of their flower-arranging competitions and headed for home. I arrived at the village just after noon. A nice pub serving homemade food took my fancy. Just my luck – too late I saw him and couldn't dodge back because he had spotted me as I entered.

'Arry was ensconced in the bar surrounded by four holiday boaters. I swear he could find them blindfold in thick fog. He was holding forth as usual, endowing his gullible audience with tales of the cut. From the tone of his voice I gathered he had already lowered a few pints of Irish rhapsody. He was leaning against the bar, a pint glass in one hand and a tot glass in the other. One of the

41

tourists had just ordered another round when 'Arry spotted me.

"Me old mate!" he greeted me at the top of his voice as if I were his bosom pal. There was no avoiding him. I hesitantly made my way over to the bar.

"Hi, 'Arry, I'm just going through to the restaurant for a meal – see you later."

I added, "If you want a lift home, I'll be about an hour."

Nice move on my part, as I dodged his attempt to hug me and shot through to the other room.

When I had finished my lunch and headed back through to the bar, 'Arry was nowhere in sight. For a minute I had a feeling of relief. A pissed-up 'Arry was all I needed in my car on my day off. Without thinking, I asked the barman, "Where is he?"

He made the universal gesture as if ejecting someone

Oh! Oh! This was going to be tricky. I considered sneaking out of the back door and making a speedy getaway. But 'Arry, although stupefied by drink, outwitted me yet again. He was sitting at one of the outside tables in the garden when I found him, keeping a wary eye on my car. No escape. I mustered up courage and approached him.

"Come on, me old mate, let's get you home."

"Yes, gotta go home," he slurred. "But I have to sort this out first." He pointed towards his parcel lying in the grass by his feet. I gathered it up and assisted him to his feet.

"Where are we off to, then, 'Arry?" I asked.

"Cobblers!" he replied.

"Don't be like that, 'Arry, I'm only trying to help."

"Cobblers!" he repeated. "I want to go to the cobblers."

I got it. He wanted the shoemakers down the road. Assisted by me with difficulty, we set off down the main street. It took all my strength to keep him upright. I had never seen 'Arry so drunk before. He kept repeating the verses of a song, "Rye whisky, leave me alone." I gathered from his attempts to sing that the tourists were American. They had evidently been feeding him some of their native hooch. The big test was to get him past the police station. As we approached I warned him, "'Arry, behave yourself now. We are near the cop shop. You know you have had trouble with these buggers before."

'Arry had been caught poaching on the lord of the manor's land on a number of occasions. I had to attend a court as his character witness once. That was a nightmare – I must tell you the saga some time.

We were virtually at the door of the station when I released him. Luckily no cops were about, thank goodness. They'd be out chasing poor innocent motorists as usual, I told myself.

"You will have to manage on your own. Stand up straight, for Jesus' sake, 'Arry, when we pass the cop shop."

He staggered, made a couple of near collapses, but fortunately grabbed something to steady himself. He supported himself in the nick of time around a constable's neck as the officer emerged from the doorway. It had to be our lucky day, for the officer was not a real copper, he was 'Kojak', a waterways security patrolman who knew 'Arry well. What is more he used to do a number of deals with him.

"Thank goodness it's you, Kojak!" I exclaimed, thankfully.

He explained, "I've just been in to report some kids throwing bricks at the boats. Lucky for you there is no one in the station except that daft clerk. What's going on?"

I answered, "I'm having a hell of a job with 'Arry. He's pissed out of his mind, been drinking with some Yanks at the boozer down the road, and they've fed him something he's not used to."

Kojak replied with alarm in his voice, "Hey come on, let's get him away from here. These buggers will have him in the cells quick as a flash. They still have it in for 'Arry after the last time. They have an idea I was mixed up in it as well. I'll be in shit if they link me to him."

I didn't know what 'the last time' was. I would have liked to have known. It always pays to have a bit of info on a security officer. Or so someone told me. Nevertheless, on this occasion I was glad of his assistance. We supported 'Arry on either side and finally got him into the cobbler's shop out of sight of the police station, in the nick of time, just as a patrol car arrived. 'Arry appeared to be recovering a little; he dumped his parcel onto the counter in front of a spotty-faced boy.

"'Ow much to mend these buggers?" he asked.

"The cobbler is not here at the moment," the boy explained.

'Arry leaned across the counter. "Are you or are you not in charge of this here shop?"

The boy hesitantly answered, "Well, me uncle says I was when he went out, so I reckon I is."

"So then you can deal with me shoes, eh?" 'Arry enquired.

"I suppose I can," the boy responded in a more affirmative manner. He undid the parcel.

"These are all for the right foot, me uncle only mends pairs."

He began to wrap them up again.

"Hey, hang on a mo," 'Arry protested. "You can't do that."

He pulled the paper off the shoes and placed two of them together.

"Say this fella was deformed and had two left feet, you would have to mend 'em cos' you can't dis, whatsists name? Yes, that's it, you are not allowed to 'criminate against poor cripples."

The boy looked uneasy. Kojak was in uniform and the Cobbler's Nephew was not quite sure whom he represented.

"OK, I'll make an exception if he is a cripple. Right, I shall call them two a pair for argument's sake. That will be a pound a pair."

"A pound a bleedin pair?" 'Arry expressed shock. "I can get a new pair from the charity shop for five bob."

"Take it or leave it, that's my uncle's usual price," the boy replied, and pushed the shoes towards 'Arry.

"Hang on a mo," 'Arry pushed them back towards him.

"How much to just heel 'em?" 'Arry enquired.

The bewildered boy answered, "Five bob."

"Ha! Then how much do you charge to sole 'em?" 'Arry asked. He had that crafty look I recognised on his face.

"Fifteen bob," the boy replied, quite proud of his mental arithmetic.

"Ha! that's more like it." 'Arry declared triumphantly. "Stick a heel from here to here," he indicated the length of the shoe. "That'll do. I'll pick em up next week."

Before the dumbfounded boy was able to reply, 'Arry was out of the shop in a flash, apparently a great deal more sober than when he entered.

In my car on the way home 'Arry explained the shoes had been his uncle's. The poor man had been wounded in the war and had only had one leg. Consequently, he only wore one shoe down. The shoes, along with some other bizarre items, were part of 'Arry's inheritance when the old guy finally popped his clogs.

I was having a pint one dinner hour when a man with a dog came into the pub accompanied by Puddling Paul, one of 'Arry's workmates. I should explain why he is so named. When there is a canal breach and the banks or canal itself require repair, the canal bottom is lined with clay to form a waterproof seal. Part of the process is known as 'clay puddling'. The work gang clomp about on the freshly laid clay to drive out the air pockets and form a watertight seal. I suppose they could be compared with the Portuguese wine treaders, the difference being that our lads wore Wellingtons.

Paul was fortunate to be born with enormous feet and was favoured by the foremen to carry out this task, hence the name. Paul was not the brightest of lads to put it kindly, but he took great pride in his puddling abilities, a task he excelled at as no brain power was needed. The other lads hated the job and swung it onto him at every opportunity. He didn't seem to mind though, especially when he was praised by the foreman and his mates. When he was younger he had left the waterways for about a year and had run away with a travelling circus. Although classed by his mates as thick, he could keep the lads entertained with some of the skills he had acquired in his time as a clown and acrobat. His party piece was his ability to walk on stilts – a useful skill when he needed to cross the cut without getting wet and something he did on many occasions, especially when tourist boats with female crews were about.

Paul was not entirely simple: he only chose to exhibit his skills as a stilt walker where he knew the canal bottom was of solid material. He had learnt this lesson the hard way. He once spent nearly an hour balanced in the middle of the cut, much to the amusement of his mates, when his stilts sank into deep mud.

Anyway, back to the story. The dog man and Paul sat down with their cronies and began relating a story. I was reading the morning paper when I heard the name "Arry' mentioned. At this point I felt the need to listen in. I leaned forward and homed in to their conversation, when I realised it was 'Arry the boatie they were discussing. It seems 'Arry had a deal with the local pet shop owner, another old ex-Welsh boatie. The man involved carried the name of 'Peter the Pet'. Peter enjoyed the reputation as an equally formidable fixer as our hero.

Actually, he was not a real born and bred boatie, for 'Arry described him as only a 'temporary' during wartime hostilities. Peter suffered with flat feet and a pierced eardrum, making him unfit for service in the armed forces. The two had once been bosom pals during the war and had crewed together on the trade boats. They dealt in anything interesting that came 'Arry's way – like grass snakes, baby rabbits, pigeons, kittens and pups, to name but a few of the reptiles, birds and animals concerned.

There had been a major falling-out between them many years ago, until one day they saw the opportunity to make a few bob and had called a truce.

The story goes as follows. Peter married a lock-keeper's widow with the unusual name of Petal. She was a very large lady with enormous proportions, but despite Peter being small and wiry, the odd couple appeared to hit it off. Both he and 'Arry had courted her in turn, vying for her favours and a comfortable and maybe erotic night in a proper bed shore-side, in her cottage. Well, despite 'Arry's unique type of courting and a stream of gifts dead and alive, Peter finally won the race to the nuptial bedchamber, much to the disgust of 'Arry. Peter's ability to read and write finally won the day. The lady required somebody capable of organising the books and paperwork of her pet shop. Since she lacked education to complete these tasks herself her logical replacement husband had to be in her words 'edificated'.

The loss of her man, who normally undertook the management of the accounts, left her in a mess and she was desperately searching for a replacement. The thwarted lover reckoned the cunning Taffy had only married her for her money and had used unfair tactics in his wooing of the luscious lady.

Peter's inheritance consisted of a substantial life insurance payment and the pet shop when Petal died a couple of years ago. But this was not the real reason the once-pals fell out. On the night of their marriage Peter took the merry ex-widow to a B&B canalside pub for their one night of honeymoon. It was an unofficial leave because of wartime restriction, leaving 'Arry to reluctantly work the pair of boats himself. The agreement the couple made was on the understanding it was strictly one night. 'Arry struggled through locks cursing his mate to all and sundry until he collapsed exhausted many miles from his loading base. Lucky for 'Arry he just happened to collapse close to a canalside pub whose manager happened to be another of his wide-ranging family. Despite pleas and threats from the controller he refused to continue until a replacement mate was dispatched. Fortunately for the pub manager none was available and he gleefully counted his increased profits. These were due entirely to 'Arry propping up the bar telling outlandish stories of life on the cut to the American servicemen. Other neighbours were not so pleased, as their vegetable patches and chicken stocks decreased as a result of 'Arry's nocturnal visitations.

Three days later Peter turned up for work with his arm in a sling and bruises all over his body. When 'Arry questioned him, he made an excuse that he had fallen down the stairs in the pub on his honeymoon night and had been in hospital ever since. 'Arry smelled a rat and probed and probed until one night when they were drunk the full story came out.

Believe it or believe it not, this is the story 'Arry spread about his mate. It was a hot summer evening when Peter and his bride retired for the night of marital bliss. Unfortunately they had both had a skinful of booze and fell asleep on top of the bed stark naked before their marriage was consummated. The next thing Peter knew he was grabbed by the wrist and went flying through the air. He landed in a heap in the corner of the room. He dragged himself up and staggered over to the bed to find his bride still fast asleep. Unable to wake her he nervously lay back on the bed. He was just about to doze off when her eyes flickered open for a split second, she reached over, gripped his arm and flung him out of the bed. Peter, astounded that his new bride should behave this way, staggered to his feet and retaliated by emptying the wash stand ewer over her. Spluttering with rage she emerged from her drink-sodden sleep and demanded to know why he had treated her in such a cruel manner. He raged that she had thrown him out of bed twice.

"My Lord," she said. "I've done it again, and I only just married you."

She explained, after swearing Peter to secrecy with the promise of equal shares in her business. She had found her first husband dead in the corner of the bedroom when she arose in the morning after a heavy boozing session. Frantic with worry but realising there would be questions asked of how he came to be dead with a broken neck in the bedroom, she made up her mind to cover her deadly deed. Petal dragged him onto the landing and tipped his body downstairs. The coroner found he had fallen downstairs in a drunken state and broken his neck. She believed until the day she died he had suffered the same nocturnal flight as Peter due to her strange habit. The lady had a recurring dream that she was picking cotton threads off her bed and throwing them out of the window. Seeing Peter's thin white arm through drunken eyes she had mistaken it for a piece of white thread. Needless to say their marriage was never consummated – rather than risk another night flight Peter slept alone in the spare room thereafter.

Anyway, back to the reason for the resumption of hostilities. All went well for a while until 'Arry discovered how much profit Peter the Pet was making on the goods he supplied, especially the pigeons. It was then that the uneasy truce that had been mutually beneficial came to an end. 'Arry, the old rogue had been laying bait for racing pigeons, capturing them, removing the rings and keeping them in his shed for a while before trading them to the pet shop. He in turn sold them on, mainly to inexperienced kids, with instructions on how to handle the birds. Of course on their first outing the birds flew back to 'Arry's shed and the procedure began again. 'Arry tried to re-negotiate the financial deal he had struck with the pet shop man to no avail.

Peter knew he had the upper hand as his establishment was the only one in the locality that 'Arry could reasonably deal with.

Outside the pet shop, tethered to a stand, was a talking parrot – the pride and joy of Peter the Pet and a great attraction to would-be customers. Any passers-by would be invited into the shop by the parrot to look around. Once inside, they very rarely escaped without purchasing something, entirely due to the pressure sale tactics of Peter the Pet.

The parrot, 'Arry decided, was Peter's weak point, but how to use the bird in his plot to seek revenge on his greedy partner? A month or so went by until the opportunity arose. One morning 'Arry's mate Puddling Paul arrived at work not in his usual cheerful manner but with a glum face. When questioned, he explained that his mother's pet parrot Bongo had been found dead that morning. Paul still lived with his mother and couldn't console her. The old woman was in the depths of despair as the bird had been her constant companion for many years. Paul couldn't afford to replace it as someone had informed him that parrots cost a bloody fortune. 'Arry went into think mode and after a few minutes he suddenly asked his mate to bring the dead bird to work the next day.

It was then, at the critical part of the story, I had to reluctantly leave the pub to attend a meeting and didn't find out what happened about the hapless bird.

A few weeks went by and I had no contact with the local workforce having been away from the district constantly. After that I had been on holiday for a fortnight. My first job on returning was to visit Puddling Paul at home as he was off work on the sick. I had to sort out an accident claim form for the union that he had made a mess of.

I knocked on the front door and heard a strange voice inviting me to 'come in and look around the shop'. This threw me for a minute, then I tried the door and it was locked. I knocked again. The same weird voice replied with an invite to enter and look around the shop. After two more attempts with the same response I decided to give up, despite the invitations. I had just closed the garden gate when Paul and his mother appeared after alighting from a bus. Paul walked painfully with the aid of two sticks. He looked a bit shocked to see me at his house.

I explained the reason for my visit and expected to be asked into the house. No chance, he took the new forms off me and made arrangements to meet in the local pub in an hour.

Looking back, I noticed they remained outside the house until I was well away before they entered. They were an odd couple, Paul and his mum, but I dealt with odd people all the time so I dismissed their weird behaviour as part of their eccentricity.

He arrived at the pub on time but with a sheepish look on his face. We had got down to business when he suddenly burst out with an apology, "Sorry I couldn't ask you into the house. Mum's a bit funny about strangers."

"Ah, don't worry," I replied. "Funny thing, I thought it was your mum that kept inviting me in, but the door was locked when I tried to open it. Who was that then? I thought only you two lived there."

Paul's face went bright red and he confessed, "Ah! It's all down to bloody 'Arry. Well! I best tell you the whole story."

I ordered another couple of pints and settled down for the continuation of the 'Arry/Parrot saga. I explained I knew his mum's parrot had died so he continued from then on. The next morning he sneaked the parrot out of the little coffin his mum had ordered him to make. He concealed it in a cardboard shoebox. Paul had to do it before she had the chance to bury him in the grave he had dug in the garden.

"My mother has our garden filled with dead animals' graves. Dogs, cats, budgies, they all have their own little plot. It's getting like the corporation cemetery, our garden."

Paul leaned forward and confidentially informed me, "She has like, a funeral service with prayers and all kinds. She even invites her old cronies to attend and they have ham sandwiches just like a real funeral. Eh! You know me dad didn't have as good a funeral as her bloody pets!"

This was getting all too much for me He was so serious and I could feel an uncontrollable fit of laughter coming on. Off he went again with his confidences.

"You know when I was a kid she buried my pet tortoise when it was hibernating. She thought the bloody thing was dead, do you see? "

I nodded sympathetically while trying to quell a laugh under the cover of a coughing spell. Paul continued, "You should have seen her face when the dog dug the bugger up in the spring and it started walking about."

Paul brought the parrot to work as instructed by 'Arry. "I didn't know what to expect, you know what 'Arry's like. I had me mum whingeing and upset and really getting me down. I thought maybe 'Arry could have brought it back to life. I know he's good with animals and the like, him being a kind of gypsy, and they know about such things, eh?

"You know they eat hedgehogs..." he confided in a whisper. What this had to do with the death of Bongo I could not see, but I sat patiently waiting for the crunch line.

"...they wrap 'em in clay to pull the spikes off and roast em," Paul explained lamely when I gave him a sceptical look.

At work he gave the box to 'Arry who disappeared with it just before knocking off time. On returning he handed the box to Paul and demanded a fiver. Paul was reluctant to pay until he detected a scratching noise in the box. When he questioned, 'Arry indicated secrecy and told him he would be well pleased when he got home and gave it to his mother. Taking a chance he paid the fiver and raced home and presented the box to his grief-stricken old mum. Before she opened it she had given him a good slapping for removing her beloved Bongo from his coffin. He persuaded her to open the box in between blows and she was delighted to find the parrot she thought dead, alive and well – despite having its beak fastened up with an elastic band.

"That was nice of 'Arry. He must have a heart after all, eh?" I interceded.

"That's not the end of it," Paul added glumly. His mum was delighted with her resurrected bird especially when it began talking when they took the elastic band off its beak. This was something it had never done before its demise.

"Trouble is the only thing the bloody thing can say is, 'Come into the shop and look around' and things like that. I daren't show my face at Peter's shop any more. One of the lads told me Peter went out to bring the stand in at closing time and his parrot was hanging upside down by its leg from its perch. It was as dead as a Dodo, stiff as a board. Funny thing! My mate told me when it had died it had changed colour a bit. Its beak had kind of shrunk as well. Eh! Here's another funny thing, Peter reckoned he heard the parrot's last words only a few minutes before it snuffed out. Do you know what he reckoned it said?"

I shook my head unable to speak. Paul took this as my desire to know the parrot's last words and whispered even lower with awe in his voice.

"It said, 'What have you got today for us, 'Arry?' Weird that, isn't it? Fancy the bugger thinking of old 'Arry just before it fell off its perch."

Oh Lord! I wished he would stop. My sides were aching trying to hold back the laughter, but he continued as I controlled my near-hysteria with difficulty.

"We was discussing it on the boat and reckon it must have been that *rigo motiss* something, eh? Like you see on them doctors' programmes on the telly. One of the lads said they had fished a body out of the canal and it was all white. That had changed colour you see? One of the lads reckons it's all the washing powder that seeps into the cut. But the parrot changed colour before it was chucked in. Strange that?"

I could imagine them sitting around in the boat's cabin at baggin debating scientific subjects. As usual there is always one of the lads an expert on something.

I had to ask, "Was 'Arry there, you know, at this debate about dead things?"

"Oh yes. He is very knowledgeable about dead things – well, he kills enough of them, doesn't he?"

"Yes, 'Arry's an expert on lots of things isn't he?" I responded cynically. After considering my reply Paul expressed his feelings for Peter the Pet.

"Poor old Peter was heartbroken I believe. He thought the

world of the bloody thing. He was so upset my mate took it away for him to give it a decent burial. Mind you Peter gave him a quid to have it seen to proper like. Didn't like to do it himself he was so upset you see. Eh! I always thought Peter a bit of a hard-nosed bugger but he was more broken up about the parrot than when his missus snuffed it.

"Eh! Do you remember his missus? Big bugger she was, wasn't she? How do you reckon Peter and her got on in bed?"

I didn't bother answering as I didn't want to get involved in the tale of the couple's honeymoon antics. The vision of her and Peter made me shudder, anyway. I pulled myself back to the present as Paul continued. This guy could certainly deviate when he told a story.

Paul looked about furtively to see if anyone was in earshot. Confirming he was not overheard he then disclosed, "Actually, it the truth be known, he chucked the bugger in the cut. I called him dead mean for doing that. But he reckons it was a proper end for a parrot seeing as the sailors used to have them. Kind of buried at sea and the parrot would have liked that."

Paul paused for a moment as if contemplating the fate of the parrot then continued.

"It was after my mate told me about these happenings that a horrible thought came to me in a flash. I bet that's where 'Arry must have got the bugger he sold to me."

"You mean out of the cut?" I questioned incredulously. I knew exactly what he meant but couldn't resist winding him up.

"No, you daft bugger," Paul gave me a strange look. He continued in a near-whisper. "I think he nicked Peter's parrot and hung me mum's dead Bongo up in its place. 'Arry says he did not and was very upset when I asked him, but I feel guilty every time I pass the shop now. I can't help it. My Mum won't part with the bird, and I'm scared of anyone coming to the house and recognising it if the bugger is Peter's bird. Bloody hell! Just imagine if Peter turned up at our house." Paul gave a kind of shudder.

"What do you reckon I should do, then?" he pleaded.

I thought for a while before asking.

"Well, how did you injure your feet, then? We best get on with this form, shall we?"

There was no way I was getting involved in one of 'Arry's Cosa Nostra type revenges.

Chapter Four
The divers

WHEN I BEGAN work on the waterways the company employed their own divers. The equipment they used was the old-fashioned hard hat with a canvas suit, big lead boots and a huge brass helmet. The two divers, nicknamed 'Tom and Jerry' after the cartoon heroes, were characters in their own right. Although they were relatives by marriage they argued continually about any subject under the sun. They took it in turns to dive, so while one of them donned the suit and disappeared into the depths the partner operated the hand-driven air pump with the help of an assistant. On a number of occasions this was 'Arry.

'Arry loved working with them and would bait them continually to instigate an argument, but his driving ambition was to don the suit and experience the thrill of being underwater, or so he alleged. The lads believed 'Arry wanted to dive because he had seen movies about divers finding masses of treasure on sunken ships. Where he would find a Spanish galleon up the cut, no one explained.

He pestered Tom and Jerry to have a go whenever they worked in the vicinity of the locks. They refused on every occasion until one day they relented when 'Arry offered them a deal they could not refuse. It had something to do with pigeons and one of 'Arry's ferrets. I was not privy to the information – for some reason it was kept secret between them.

It was a lovely summer's day and the diving duo were working at my lock repairing some of the underwater machinery. At lunchtime the divers agreed to dress 'Arry in the suit but with the proviso he was not allowed to actually dive in deep water. They only permitted him to stand on the ladder hooked to the side of the diving boat and climb down until the water just lapped over his head. 'Arry agreed to the conditions and was as excited as a birthday kid. They squeezed him into the thick canvas suit with difficulty. Tom decided the lead boots were not necessary as he wasn't going down too far but 'Arry insisted on them fitting the chest weights and lead-laden belt so he could get the feel of what it was like to be a real diver. Fully dressed, 'Arry, with a broad grin on his face, hung on the ladder waiting for the helmet to be fitted. The rest of the lads stood on the lockside enjoying the spectacle and shouting insults and encouragement to their mates.

Tom fitted the helmet and Jerry stood by the air pump – there was only one part of the equipment left to fit and that was the glass in the front of the helmet. Tom asked 'Arry with a knowing sneer, because he knew from experience this was where other would-be divers gave up and bottled out, "You all right, 'Arry? This is it – you're not panicking, are you?"

'Arry gave him the thumbs-up sign. Tom had turned around to get the glass when 'Arry stepped off the ladder and sank like a stone. Talk about panic! Considering the size of 'Arry and the weight of the gear it took the combined strength of all of the lads to drag him to the surface.

'Arry was fortunate that day: he survived. We dragged him onto the quayside and rolled him belly down. Water poured out of the helmet opening. With a struggle Tom unscrewed the helmet, 'Arry gurgled, coughed, spewed up and recovered in an instant. We knew he was okay when he began playing merry hell with the divers as if they had been responsible for the near disaster.

We stripped him of the rest of the diving gear and I took him into the lock hut to recover and dry out. He was sitting sipping a cup of tea when I asked him, "Why did you step off the ladder, 'Arry? In fact, why did you want to dive, anyway?"

He looked around furtively making sure none of the other lads were within earshot.

"Eels," he replied, by way of explanation.

Astounded I enquired, "Eels, 'Arry? What have they got to do with you wanting to dive?"

"I can trust you, Scouse – you're not a money-grabbin' bugger like them lot and you won't move in on one of my little, er, schemes."

He paused then insisted, "Will you?"

I assured him, "I have no intention of moving in on your rackets..."

He glared disapprovingly at the use of the word 'rackets'.

I amended it to "...little money-making schemes."

He nodded and continued, "You know them German ships that come up the river?"

"Yes."

"You know I have that old freezer of yours on my boat?"

"Yes. I don't know what you wanted that for. The motor's knackered and you couldn't use it on your boat anyway, because you've no electric."

"Ha, Scouse, I knew you didn't understand. It's not the freezer part I wanted. I just needed a big box with a tight lid that holds water, you see?"

"Oh, I see," I replied. I still hadn't caught onto the plot yet.

"You know I get eels out of the river with my traps?"

"Yes."

"Those Germans, they like eels don't they? I seen it on the telly, the buggers eats nothing but sausages, eels and some smelly cabbage stuff."

"Well, I'm not sure that's quite right, 'Arry, but go on, I'm intrigued."

"Now them ships only come up here say every other week, yes?"

"Yes, that's right – about every ten days to be exact."

"Exactly is right. Now my idea is this I catch the eels, put them in the old freezer and flog 'em to the Germans when they come up here – nice one, eh?"

I had to congratulate him for his ingenuity. "Hmm, sounds a good idea to me, 'Arry. "

I added admiringly, "You're a smart bugger, all right, but why keep them in the old freezer? I still don't understand."

He explained, "They have to be alive or the Germans won't 'ave 'em. They likes to kill 'em and smoke 'em themselves. I don't know why. Who cares, anyway, as long as the sods buy 'em?"

At this point 'Arry went into a kind of dream state, and he said, more to himself than me. "That smoking lark – I'll have to find out how the buggers do that. I could make a few more bob if I sold the eels already smoked. I've tried askin' the cooks on the ships but the higorant buggers don't speak English. Eh, Scouse, imagine that – goin' through life not being able to speak English!"

I urged him on to divulge the rest of the plot, and he continued, "So I fills the freezer with water out of the river. Tap water's no good – they don't like fresh water, it has to be from where the buggers live. I need a tight lid 'cos eels can escape. Tried 'em in a barrel once and they all got out overnight. Did you know they can cross land? They wait until it rains and slip across the grass. I've seen the crafty buggers doin' it meself."

"Right, 'Arry, I understand now – but why did you want to dive, especially at the end of the lock?"

"You know I catch the most eels from above and below the lock and sluices?"

"Yes."

"Well, I figures if I got into a diver's suit and had a look underwater like, I could see where the buggers hide and set my traps there."

I asked, tongue in cheek, "Well, did you?"

He gave me a funny look and asked, "Did I what?"

"Did you spot the eels' hiding place?"

'Arry looked glum. "No chance, couldn't see a bloody thing down there, I was too busy trying to breathe. I wouldn't get into a diver's suit again for a big clock."

I replied with relief, "Well, thank goodness for that, 'Arry. I can't take any more traumas for a while. We would have all been in the shit with Pontius and your Cissie if you'd snuffed it, you know."

My concern appeared to embarrass 'Arry and he mumbled, "I don't know how those stupid divers work with all that water in the bloody helmet; they must have special noses or something. It near killed me. I'm not doing that again, I can tell you."

I didn't enlighten 'Arry that he wasn't fully equipped when he took his memorable first and last dive

So that was the end of 'Arry's diving career. On that fateful occasion, one of his 'enterprises' nearly cost him his life.

A couple of months later we had another drama. The divers were on the way home in the works bus. The driver told me the story at the funeral.

Tom and Jerry were arguing as usual, then suddenly Tom went quiet. Despite Jerry's baiting Tom did not respond. The lads who normally enjoyed the entertainment assumed he had either lost the latest argument with his brother-in-law and given up, or had fallen asleep.

Some of the lads were prone to do this on their way home especially the day after the monthly darts night.

The bus reached the place where Tom usually alighted. For a joke, Jerry persuaded the bus driver not to wake him until he arrived back at the depot. The driver dropped everyone off at their usual places and took the bus to the depot. It was only when he shook Tom that he discovered that the poor guy was well and truly dead.

Jerry never got over the loss of his adversary. He could not get on with anyone else. Within a month he applied for and received early retirement. The result of the loss of divers was the curtailment of routine maintenance and the use of diving contractors on a 'fail and fix' basis.

The first emergency that required a diver arrived. The problem was a blockage on the lock sill. I was pleased to see the divers because they were two men I had worked with years before on a salvage job on the Mersey. Like Tom and Jerry they were characters and had nicknames. To their friends and workmates they were known as 'Snitch' the leading diver and 'Snatch' his second man and back-up diver. Both men had trained and served in the Royal Navy together as clearance and demolition divers during World War Two.

Unlike our own divers they had modern frogmen's equipment

that utilised a powered compressor on land feeding air to the divers via long hoses. On occasions when the situation warranted it they used a backpack bottle. The difference between these two and Tom and Jerry was they didn't argue but were full of fun and a fund of great stories, usually about their exploits in the navy.

I remember I was once manning a diving tender when the divers were working on a dry dock gate. Snitch was fresh out of the navy – it was his first civilian job. The procedures they used were a lot different from those they had followed in the navy. Instead of loading up with weights the divers were pulling themselves down to the bottom using the dock wall. Snitch surfaced after a dive and showed us one of his fingers, which was bleeding heavily. While I bandaged it and covered the finger with a piece of rubber glove he explained what happened.

"As I was pushing myself down I put my hand in a hole in the wall to get a grip and something bit me."

We laughed and Snatch called him 'a lying bugger'. To prove it was true he insisted his mate went down with him to have a look – divers can communicate with each other if they touch helmets. They went down together and reached the area where the hole was supposed to be. Snatch asked his mate to point out where the hole was and unbelievably Snitch stuck the finger of his other hand in to indicate where he had been bitten. When he surfaced I had to bandage his other hand. Poor Snitch never lived that one down.

The day they arrived 'Arry and Paul were on passage with their boat and got delayed at the lock while the divers undertook the repairs. They stood fascinated on the quay watching the divers working. 'Arry had never seen this kind of diving operation and asked question after question.

"Who are they and what are they up to, Scouse?"

I explained, "They have come to examine the bottom of the gates. I'm having trouble getting a mitre and a good seal; there might be something on the sill."

'Arry asked another question. "Ah, but who are they – I mean what's their names?"

I replied wearily, "The divers are from Liverpool, 'Arry; they are known to their pals as Snitch and Snatch."

Paul evidently found the names funny and laughed.

'Arry enquired, "What you laughing at, daft arse?"

Paul stopped laughing and asked, "Is that their real name, Scouse, honest?"

Snitch was just donning the last of his equipment ready to make a dive. Snatch was a big powerful man with bare arms completely covered in tattoos and he answered Paul in a menacing way: "Yes, 'course it's our name. Never heard names like that before lad? Think its funny, eh, lad?"

Paul replied in a scared voice, "No Mister, I haven't. I mean, I don't."

Snatch asked, "Don't what, lad?"

Paul replied, "I don't know, Mr Snatch."

Snitch was about to don his mask. He ordered Snatch to start up the compressor and turn the speaker on. When it was running satisfactorily Snitch fixed his mask, tossed a weighted line into the water and jumped into the lock after it.

Snatch whispered to him, "Snitch's Dad had a big nose so he called him..." Before he finished the explanation Paul answered, "Snitch! I get it."

"And my pals in the navy called me Snatch because I used to say during the war 'I nearly copped it that time – I was only snatched from the jaws of death by a miracle'."

I smiled; I knew that was the sanitised version but Paul, not being a Scouser or a sailor, wouldn't have twigged the original much cruder joke.

I introduced my mates to Snatch.

'Arry told him in a confidential manner, "Done a bit of diving, meself, you know? Course it was in proper gear, with the big helmet and lead boots – not this fancy crap you're usin'."

Snatch looked impressed. Paul and I looked amazed.

'Arry carried on, "Yes, I remember the last time I dived it was at this very lock. My so-called assistants bloody near killed me."

He shuddered visibly and dramatically.

"If I hadn't had my wits about me on that day I think yours truly would have passed on to the great beyond."

I have never heard 'Arry waxing so lyrical and telling such blatant lies; there had to be a reason – he had a plan in mind.

He continued, "To be honest that's why I gave up divin' – you can't get the reliable assistance. Now, take you two, for instance, you seem to have it right."

Ha! The flattery! We are getting there, slowly but surely, any minute now.

"Hmmm – you know when you are down there is it very clear, the water? I mean I couldn't see a thing through that old-fashioned gear I was usin'."

'Arry failed to tell Snatch he was only under for seconds and was at the time gasping for air.

Snatch replied, "It's not too bad – not as bad as in some places I've dived. If the sun is bright like today and we are working in water not too deep we can see pretty good. But you being a diver know about this, eh, 'Arry?"

'Arry responded, "Yes, I know what you mean."

He continued probing.

"So you reckon your mate can see pretty good today, eh? Tell you what, do us a favour when he comes up – will you ask him if he can see any fish down there, especially eels?"

A garbled voice emitted from a speaker box. Paul leapt backward with fright. 'Arry said in a startled voice, "Bloody hell – where did that come from?"

I explained, "It's the diver, 'Arry."

'Arry replied with disbelief. "What are you telling me, he speaks under water? I would never have believed it if I hadn't heard it with my own eyes."

Snatch smiled and threw a switch. He spoke into the box, and his partner replied again. I couldn't understand what the diver was saying.

Snatch interpreted his partner's report.

"Snitch has cleared the sill; there was a lump of metal on it that must have been dropped off a barge or ship. He's secured it to the line – that's the good news. The bad news is, it's broke a lump off the sill. He wants to know, have you any more instructions before he comes up?"

Before I could get out the words, "Can you fix it?" 'Arry interrupted, "Eh, Snatch, me old mate. If that's your mate talking, ask him about the fish – especially the eels."

Snatch pressed the switch and conveyed the message. A garbled reply burst from the speaker.

Snatch told 'Arry, "He said there is loads of them down here – if he only had a net he could fill it for you."

'Arry was beside himself with excitement.

"I'll get him one at dinner hour. Oh boy, this is great – how big does he want the net?"

Another message was passed, another reply was received. Snatch translated the gobbledegook: "As big as you can get, 'Arry."

He turned to me, "Now, Scouse, about this piece broken off the sill? We can fix it if we have the stuff in the van that I know will put it right. Shall I tell him to measure the job then he can come up? I'll go and look for the gear."

I agreed. After a few minutes Snitch surfaced and climbed the wall ladder.

He stripped his mask off and reported on his findings. While his mate went to check if the mixture was in the van we pulled the offending lump of metal out of the lock. I recognised it as a length of rubbing strake off a barge. We decided to finish the job after lunch. 'Arry disappeared aboard his boat with Paul and within minutes they were sailing up river at speed.

The two divers stripped their gear and left in the van. I went home for lunch. The divers were first back – something amused them but they wouldn't let me in on it. They had the mixture already in a bucket ready to fix the sill.

'Arry arrived back at the lock with a red net onion bag with a capacity of half a hundredweight. He showed it to the divers and asked, "Is it big enough?"

Snatch replied doubtfully, "I suppose it will have to do if that's all you've got. Come on, lads, got work to do."

While Snitch dressed, Snatch started the compressor. He moved the bucket containing the mixture to the lock side and tied it to the rope. The diver fitted his mask and jumped back into the lock. The speaker squawked again. Snatch lowered the loaded bucket into the lock.

Another squawk emitted from the box.

Snatch explained, "He wants a bucket of water to mix the gunge. Hey, sunshine, nip over to the tap and fill this up for me, there's a good lad – and hurry up before the gunge goes off."

He handed the bucket to Paul. Paul raced off to do his bidding.

'Arry pleaded, "Ask him if he can he see the fish!"

A conversation took place between divers. Snatch assured 'Arry that there were plenty down there. He said to send the net and he would fill it. 'Arry, with fumbling fingers, placed a stone in the net, tied it to a line and lowered it into the lock.

The speaker squawked. Snatch in an amazed voice told us, "Wow, he reckons there is salmon – bloody hell, I've never seen them this far inland!"

'Arry begged, "What, what's he saying?"

Snatch explained, "He reckoned there is tuna and yes – I thought I heard him right – sardines! Wow, this is some river!"

He looked crestfallen as he informed 'Arry, "He's not mentioned any eels though, 'Arry. Sorry mate."

'Arry retorted, "Bugger the eels. Salmon is worth more than any eels any day. Tell him to load the net and send it up."

"We'll have to do the job first, 'Arry. Plenty of time after the job is done – the fish ain't going anywhere, are they?"

Paul returned, carefully carrying a full bucket. Snatch attached it to the line and lowered it into the lock. Another squawk, he hauled the bucket up, emptied the water out and asked Paul for another bucket. Off raced Paul.

This procedure was repeated about ten times until Paul collapsed, absolutely knackered. He still didn't twig what was going on and I couldn't bring myself to tell him he was being wound up.

After about an hour Snatch reported, "Snitch has the job half-finished. He's coming up for a while – the gunge takes time to go off. He will have to go back later to check it and maybe add some more."

'Arry impatiently asked, "What about the fish? Ask him – should we pull the net up?"

Communication took place.

Snatch ordered, "Pull her up, 'Arry."

It took the combined the strength of Paul and 'Arry to recover the net. 'Arry was beside himself with joy.

That is until the net broke the surface and they dragged it, streaming water, onto the lockside. The weight in the net was the bucket full of water; in the bucket was a tin of salmon, a tin of tuna, and a tin of sardines in tomato sauce.

Later in the afternoon 'Arry got his revenge. He noticed the divers' telephone number on their van. He also observed both divers were wearing pagers on their belts. When Snatch donned the diving gear after lunch and prepared to dive, his pager buzzed. 'Arry was nowhere about. Snatch stripped off his gear, pressed the button on his pager then donned the gear again.

Four times this occurred until he cursed and threw the pager into the river. He never twigged it was 'Arry setting him up from the lock hut. When he finally dived I noticed 'Arry had appeared and was lurking by the compressor. I didn't see him do it but when Snatch surfaced he informed me, "Eh, Scouse, them flowers in your garden ain't half got a powerful scent. I can even smell 'em when I'm on the bottom. I've never experienced that before."

It was only after they left on completing the job that 'Arry admitted he had squirted one of those bathroom pong masker aerosols near the compressor inlet.

The divers were always good for a laugh when they arrived to work on the locks...

Chapter Five
The big debates

THE LADS WERE sitting in the lock hut Monday morning having their baggin.

They were telling the usual lies about their fantastic weekend. Brickface told us he'd had to give his kids a good telling off. I could see he wanted to unburden himself and encouraged him to tell all. He was moaning about his kids, something he didn't usually do, as he was very proud of his brood.

"They had been to a place in the city with their granddad and bought all kinds of junk," he opened his tale. Brickface was always complaining about the tricks his dad got up to and the way he got his kids involved – they were usually the innocents led astray by the old man.

"What's he done, now?" one of the lads asked. It was common knowledge that whenever his dad, a retired canal man we all knew well, was involved with his grandsons there was usually a good story to be told.

Brickface explained, "I was doing a bit of a job for him and my old lady. The kids were a pain, causing me lots of grief. He offered to take them out of the way. That's OK and I was glad of it but it's where he took them that I object to."

"Where?" we inquired.

"The old bugger only took 'em to the Wizard's Den, and gave them money to spend there while he had a pint."

My ears pricked up at the name 'Wizard's Den'. We all knew Brickie was a bit of a prude and he showed it on many occasions. When the lads were telling jokes or dirty stories he usually left their company.

So the Wizard's Den was still up and running. The place had been there since I was a kid and what was more, I didn't know it still existed.

In my opinion they sold some of the most fantastic magic tricks and joke packs a kid could dream of.

"Still going, eh, Brickie, the old Wizards Den? It's a great place. What did the kids get that's annoyed you so much?" I asked.

"Well, apart from itching powder which drove us all nuts, we thought we had shingles or something 'orrible. My missus was all for going to the doctor until we found the packets. The little sods had even put the bloody stuff on the dog and cat. Them poor sods were scratching their arses off. Cost us two quid at the vets. I'm taking that out of their pocket money I can tell you. Then there was the snakes that popped out of tins and frightened the crap out of the missus," he added glumly. "They weren't the worst things they got though. The little sods bought Dr Windbag's Extreme Fart Powder. Bloody hell, was me and my missus embarrassed, I can tell you!"

The lads leaned forward and demanded more. There was none more eager than 'Arry to learn of the magic powers of Dr Windbag.

I remembered it from old. It was powerful stuff even then, but Brickie was referring to 'Extreme' Fart Powder, and that must be something else. I had to know about it.

He continued with the saga.

"We had my wife's two old widow aunts and the retired priest, vicar, or monk – I'm not sure what he is, but he was something to do with God. Anyway we had them over for Sunday tea. They are a bit of a pain, but I've got to treat them right. The missus is their only living relative. The old girls live in that big house by the sea at Southport."

"Eh! I've seen that place – it must be worth a fortune." I remarked.

Brickie nodded, confirmed my observation and continued.

"The place is full of antiques, it's a bit like a museum. They have really expensive oil paintings all over the walls by real proper artists. Not them print things you get from Woollies, you understand? Then there's cupboards full of bone china. No modern crap furniture, either, they have lots of really old stuff. My missus reckons she saw gear like it when she visited one of those stately homes with the WI."

Brickie disclosed this last bit of information in a hushed voice as if to stress the value of his would-be inheritance. The lads gasped admiringly on cue. A kind of dreamy expression passed over his face. Shaking himself out of his reverie he carried on.

"They are both in their eighties, the old girls, both seen their husbands off years ago. Their husbands were brothers, had something to do with banking. You know they married sisters, strange, that, eh? Now they live together. Both of them sold their other houses and they were a bit tasty, I can tell you. Anyway they moved into that big house together. Silly sods should have bought a nice little bungalow and gave my missus one of their houses, seeing as she is their only relative. Don't you think?"

We all nodded wisely and agreed. Brickie carried on with his tale of woe.

"They are filthy rich but tight as fishes' arses. They won't spend a penny if they can avoid it, know what I mean?"

"What about the vicar fella?" one of the lads asked. "Is he giving them one?"

I knew sooner or later sex would rear its ugly head, it usually did in these debates, we all leaned forward expectantly. Brickie looked appalled at this suggestion. "Don't be so stupid, they're in their eighties. Anyway, I don't think they have ever had sex even when they were married – they never had any kids and they wouldn't have had anything to do with birth control. They're proper Catholics. I supposed they took the Pope's advice on how to go about it."

Paul contributed some of his knowledge in a conspiratorial manner.

"I believe those Catholics won't wear packamacs when they are at it."

Brickie enquired impatiently, "What are you on about now, Paul? What have packamacs got to do with what I am telling you lot?"

Paul replied sheepishly, "I thought it would help to explain things. You know Mick, that fella who works in the repair yard? Well he's Irish and has got eight kids and another one on the way. I heard one of the fitters tell him he should try wearing a packa-mac when he is giving his old woman one. I thought it was funny, but that's what they do to stop having kids. Anyway Mick told him he wasn't allowed to because the Pope has forbid it."

Brickie threw his hands up in a gesture of despair.

"Oh God, will some one explain it to him, please? I haven't got the time to give him sex education. Just shut up for a while, Paul, will you?"

'Arry backed him up. "Yes, button up Paul, you're a daft bug-ger. I want to hear about this tea party Go on, Brickie, let's hear the end of it. Pilot will be here soon."

Brickie continued where he left off.

"Where was I before I was so rudely interrupted by that loony? Oh yes! I remember what I was telling you about. The probing priest or whatever he is? Funny the way they always drag that old bugger with them, though. I'm sure he's trying to get his feet under their table. We can't get to talk about things with him there. Nosy old sod is always asking questions. He wants to know the ins and outs of a duck's arse. All me and my missus are trying to do is stop them leaving everything to that bloody cats' home – or to him," he added sullenly.

We all nodded wisely and wished we had his luck without the hindrance of the holy Joe. Brickie continued painting the picture of his Sundays when the trio visited his house for tea.

"My missus makes us all dress in our Sunday best. Me, I would have sooner been messing around in my shed. The kids are really pissed off. They hate all this dressing-up lark, but my missus insists saying we will all benefit eventually. Anyway, we was sat in the best parlour drinking tea from the special Wedgwood china tea service we bought off the barge lads, remember them?"

We all knew about the tea services purchased off the barge lads, as we all had bought sets ourselves. As I recall, 'Arry bought, or should I say 'traded', for ten sets but him and his wife still drank tea out of enamel mugs. Knowing him, he outwitted us all and made a good profit on that deal.

Brickie glumly carried on with his tale.

"My missus had really done them proud. We had Earl Grey tea and lemon."

'Arry interceded, "What the hell is that?"

Brickie explained proudly, "It's what the posh buggers drink. No tea bags, it has to be real tea leaves. We have a little sieve thing, it's very smart, made of silver. My Aunty bought it for my missus' birthday. Eh, lads, you'll find this hard to believe. They don't have milk in the stuff, no not them, only lemon juice. Would you believe that?"

'Arry looked on in disbelief.

Brickie moaned on, "She had even bought Madeira cake from that fancy baker's shop in the High Street."

Puddling Paul interrupted, "Dear buggers, them in that shop. You can get the same stuff from the Kwiki at half the price. I know, 'cos my mum gets it there."

Brickie gave him a scornful glare and continued, "It's their favourite, you know? They have to have best butter on it, not bloody marg like we do."

The lads tut-tutted understandingly. Brickie sighed and whinged on about the expense of the visits.

"Best about it, I hate the bloody stuff myself, sooner have a jam scone. Eh! And she had only made little cucumber sarnies."

We nodded approvingly.

'Arry snorted. "Phew! I had some of them useless things at the mission when my old woman popped her clogs. Wouldn't feed a flea, them things. I like big butties me, yeah! Something you can get your teeth into, know what I mean?"

We laughed as 'Arry didn't have a tooth in his head. He was the only man I knew that slapped everything he ate between slices of thick bread, including meat pies. I don't know how he managed without gnashers but he could out-eat the rest of us. I suppose he had hard gums.

Brickie gave him a look of disdain for interrupting his flow and carried on.

"Anyway, all was going well, we were getting around to inheritance talk, making wills, life insurance and the likes, when the Holy Joe reached over to the cake stand for another slice of Madeira.

"That's another thing that really gets to me. My missus insisted we have one of those old fashioned cake stands, you know them three-tier things? She had seen one in an old picture and she gave me no peace until I got her one. Cost a bloody fortune it did, we only use it when the old ladies visit. The bloody cat sleeps on it for the rest of the time. I ask you, a bloody stand to put cakes on? I get a scone slapped in my hand and like it."

At this point Brickie went quiet and his face reddened even more than usual, I'm not sure whether it was anger or embarrassment. I gave him a few discreet seconds to gather his thoughts, then sympathetically urged him on. Hesitantly he disclosed the punch line to the story.

"Oh yes, this is where I really got upset," Brickie paused, then divulged the secret we had all been waiting for in a rush.

"The old bugger let out this enormous fart. I mean it was tremendous. I was gob-smacked, I don't mind telling you. Fancy a holy man doing that in front of ladies!"

Pretending shock, we gasped.

"The rude old bugger looked at my old dog Prince – he was only trying to blame him, cheeky sod. This is the worst thing though. You know what my lad said?"

We knew what was coming next, but feigning ignorance we asked him to reveal what the boy remarked.

"'More tea, Vicar?' I mean fancy saying that? It gets worse. The two old women started farting in unison. Bloody hell! The farts were so powerful I swear they hovered about a foot off their chairs. One of them had our cat on her knee and the poor bugger leapt off, squawked in terror and hid under the sideboard. It's like a night out at the bloody Philharmonic. My missus is no better, she joins in with a high kind of squeaking from her backside. I suppose she was out of tune 'cos she had only drunk one cup of the bloody tea. Every one is apologising and farting at the same time. It's chaos I can tell you. The kids are rolling around the floor

71

laughing their stupid heads off. I think the sods put it in the teapot 'cos it didn't affect me. I only drink coffee and the kids were drinking pop. They swore they didn't, but I found the empty packet in the bin next day and knew they had done it. Anyway, the three guests requested me to drive them home. What a bloody journey that was, I can tell you. If I could have connected them up, I could have driven without petrol. If the old women find out it was down to my kids, I'll be out of the will for sure, and that farting old friar will be in like a shot."

When the laughter had died down and the lads were heading out to work, 'Arry asked Brickface. "Have your kids got any more of that stuff? I'll buy it off 'em if they have any."

"No bloody fear," Brickie responded indignantly. "The little sods had ten packets – they owned up when I threatened to stop their pocket money. They were going to fix the teacher's tea on Monday. I threw all them bloody packets down the bog and flushed them away. I bet the rats are farting themselves to death down the sewers."

Was I having a mad moment or what? I told the lads, "I'm going up there next week to a meeting. I'll be near the Wizard's Den and I want to call in myself for old times' sake."

'Arry approached me when he found me on my own.

"Eh, Scouse, you say you're going near that there Wizard's Den place Brickie was on about. Do us a favour, pal. Pick us up a few packets of that there farting stuff, will you?"

After considering his request and asking a few questions I offered to get him what he required, but first he had to tell me what he wanted it for.

"Ah! Don't you worry, my old mate," he replied to assure me. "It won't affect you, I just want to play a joke on someone that's got it coming. Know what I mean?" 'Arry tapped the side of his nose secretively.

"You'll have to give me some cash, then," I ordered. Knowing 'Arry from old I wanted cash in advance.

"Bloomin' heck!" he responded angrily. "Don't you trust me or what?"

He thought for a moment, and I could see there was no cash

coming my way.

"Tell you what, I'll fix you up when you get back. If I don't pay up, you don't give me the goods, fair enough?"

With some hesitation I agreed to his conditions, feeling I had been outwitted yet again.

I did indeed visit the famous Wizard's Den and had a great half hour catching up with all the latest scary and funny gadgets. I purchased two packets of the Doctor Windbag's Extreme Fart Powder. It was a week or so until I caught up with 'Arry and delivered his order. Of course we had the usual haggling about the cost. He offered to trade a pair of slaughtered rabbits which I declined and insisted on being paid in cash. Not to be outdone 'Arry took the rest of the day to complete the deal. He didn't dip into his pocket to pay. 'Arry traded the rabbits for a gallon of red lead paint with a Danish seaman as the ship passed through the lock. The paint was in turn traded to the local blacksmith for a handmade fire iron. The fire iron was traded to the pub landlord for two leather straps embellished with original horse brasses. One of the straps of horse brasses were traded with the carpenter for a birdbox which 'Arry knew I fancied for my garden as a birthday present for my wife.

At four o'clock the deals were completed. I didn't get the cash I insisted on at the outset but finished up with a handsome addition to my garden and a happy wife. 'Arry was content because yet again he had proved his ability to outwit me. He also had a strap embellished with original horse brasses to add to his trade goods.

The fart powder. Well, I believe I finally found out who 'Arry had in mind when he requested the deadly potion, although he denied it when I confronted him. I am not sure if it was a pre-planned revenge attack or the opportunity just arose and he took it.

It had been 'Arry's habit to scrounge a cup of tea and a goodly handful of his favourite dunking chocolate biscuits from the porter-cum-caretaker whenever he tied up his boat on the wharf by the office. All went well for years and 'Arry enjoyed his tea, biscuits and gossip. The caretaker and some of the office staff had the benefit of 'Arry's trade goods. That is until a new manager came on the scene, who was very quickly bestowed with the title of 'The Chopper'. He introduced a pass-only policy for entering the offices which immediately excluded the likes of 'Arry

For the office staff, a tea and coffee vending machine was installed with a pay-as-you-pour system. For the manager, he kept his own private fancy Italian coffee percolator.

It took 'Arry at least a week to figure out how to bypass the security system. He found an emergency exit located in a little-used storeroom.

With a few adjustments to the locking device 'Arry could enter and leave the office at leisure, so it was business as usual for his trade goods but no tea and chocolate biscuits, much to 'Arry's annoyance.

Unfortunately for us Chopper's background was military with no previous experience of the civilian waterways. He certainly did not understand the intricate ways of the cut or the unique work-force. He came in with one aim in mind – to reduce costs and reor-ganise the rabble of a workforce on military lines. I gleaned from a reliable source that these were the ideas he put forward at his interview. Big mistake – it had taken a hundred years or so to cre-ate such a rabble, and one man in a single lifetime had no chance.

The lads were getting really pissed off with him. He appeared all over the place without warning, interfering, threatening and generally spoiling the happy lot of the workforce. 'Arry particu-larly hated him as he was upsetting his business by his sudden appearances. Pontius continually moaned that he was having his authority undermined as Chopper countermanded his orders.

After settling into his new job for a couple of weeks Chopper's first task was to gather the workforce together at the workshop and inform us of his intentions. He made no bones about it, he did not believe in trade unions and had no intention of dealing with them.

He began the meeting by issuing a string of orders. The work-force from now on would wear their supplied uniforms at all times to identify them. The issued boots would be cleaned and polished.

Someone at the back shouted, "Bollocks to that bullshit, I had enough of that in my national service."

The manager enquired angrily, "Who said that? What did you say?"

The wag, hidden by his huddle of workmates, retorted, "I said we should fit some bollards to give a better service to the boaters."

The manager replied with a smile – I am not sure of relief or approval. "Excellent idea."

He went on to instruct us, "I expect you chaps to turn out smartly attired and promptly on all occasions. Absences and lateness will not be tolerated without a medical certificate."

When he finally finished laying down the law to the gob-smacked lads, he asked for questions.

Cynically I asked, "Will we only salute yourself and senior management but not the foremen – them being like NCOs?"

The idiot replied seriously after considering it for a moment, "Good question, that man. I have a feeling by your question you have served in the military and appreciate the benefits of showing respect to superiors. Although I think it would be useful and beneficial for discipline, we will waive the saluting. Don't let my refusal to utilise your idea dampen your enthusiasm. If you have any other good ideas I am introducing a suggestion scheme with rewards. I want to encourage all of you to participate in it. Hand your suggestions to the foreman on pay days. He will vet them, if he approves the suggestion he will forward them on to me for consideration.

"Now, unknown to you chaps I have been observing some of your so-called work practices. For example on three occasions I have taken passage on a ship navigating the river. When I passed the site of the piling and the dredger I noticed a distinct lack of activity."

Someone shouted, "He's a bloody spy!"

The manager snarled, "What was that you said?"

His accuser answered, "I was asking, 'Do we have to wear a tie?'"

Chopper answered, "I have decided only lock keepers, bridge

keepers and foremen will be wearing ties as part of their uniform."

He pointed at 'Arry, Al and Sam.

"You three were actually lounging about smoking and drinking tea when I passed by, and before you say it…" he gave a knowing smirk "…it was not an official meal break. In future this will not be tolerated. If anyone is observed being idle he will be on a charge!"

The lads gasped and began muttering. 'Arry complained to me, "Ow much is he goin' to charge us? I'm not paying the bugger nowt, he can sod off."

The manager evidently overheard him and hurriedly amended his threat. "I shall rephrase that, of course I mean a 'disciplinary.'"

It was at this point I decided this man was a nut and I should turn the lads loose on him. Let's see how he could deal with a bout of intellectual sparring. Usually when we had one of these types of meetings I tried to keep the lads under control, but not on this occasion.

He continued ranting on, "This could lead to suspension or even dismissal."

One of the senior dredger crew, a well-known loyal company's man, pointed out, "Sir, with all due respect. We have to stop dredging, pull to one side and drop the wires to let the ships pass in the channel."

Al also explained on behalf of his gang, "We have to stop working because it's a safety hazard to continue piling when a craft is passing."

He added in a lowered voice, "Any bugger with half a brain knows that."

The manager gave a snort of disdain.

"Piffling excuses! Always excuses! The civilian chaps of this country will have to mend their ways if we are to compete internationally with our rivals. You must have heard about the excellent productivity of the Japanese and German workers – they could do all of your jobs more efficiently. For your information when I was in the services we carried on with our duties regardless. Even under enemy fire, if the situation warranted it."

One of the lads, Old Wilf, who been around since the year dot and was a time-served soldier before joining the waterways, asked, "And where was that, then?"

"Where was what?" the obviously harassed manager replied.

"What arena of warfare were you in when you carried on your duties under fire? You look too young for World War Two and even too young for Korea."

The manager replied, "I was speaking hypothetically, of course."

Old Wilf asked, "So you have never seen action then. What regiment was you in anyway?"

The manager did not answer.

Wilf whispered to me, "I bet this bugger was in the Pay Corp – he looks like a chair-bound wallah. See if you can find out, Scouse."

Alarmed, I whispered back, "How the bloody hell am I supposed to find that out, Wilf?"

He tapped the side of his nose and replied in a conspiratorial manner, "Tha knows, Scouse, we know you have pals that can find out anything about anyone."

Sometimes I thought the lads believed I had some kind of intelligence unit specialising in solving some of the weird questions they continually asked me.

One of the lads, a hothead, shouted from behind the saw bench where he was enjoying a joint, "Sod him, silly bugger. Let's go on strike. That'll show him."

The manager virtually screamed, "Who said anything about a strike?"

The dopy hothead replied, "I said I enjoyed the rugger and I have to get back to work on my bike."

Roars of laughter followed his remark. The manager had lost control of the meeting.

We now had him on a wrong foot. He was looking to make a strategic withdrawal, to use an army expression. Politely I raised my hand. I moved in ready with a killer question knowing how it would incense the lads. He gratefully invited me to speak and I enquired sarcastically, "So what you are telling us is that you have heard that the Japanese or the Germans or some other foreigners are threatening to come over here and take over our jobs?"

'Arry shouts, "There is no Japanee going to get my bloody boat, I can tell you that for nothing."

Chaos was building up nicely, with side meetings and debates taking place. The ex-servicemen were really getting excited about their former enemy taking over their jobs.

The manager glared at me and kind of frothed at the mouth, making unrecognisable noises.

I quickly added, "I'm going to get onto the personnel manager about this. Fancy him knowing about this and not informing us our jobs are under threat by foreigners. Lads, it looks like they are breaking the deal we have under the national agreement."

One of the shop stewards advised, "I think we should also let our three Members of Parliament know about this right away, don't you lads?"

Brickie added, "We should notify the local council. If we are to have loads of foreigners moving in around here where are they going to live? There is already a housing shortage."

A roar of approval greeted the suggestions.

The manager's face turned a bright red. He pointed at me with a wavering finger and exclaimed, "I never mentioned Japanese or Germans, what are you on about?"

Like an audience of kids at a pantomime, fifty voices chanted, "Oh yes, you did."

The manager was in retreat and sheepishly admitted, "Well, I did mention them but you are taking it completely out of context."

His expression changed as if a switch had been thrown reconnecting his brain. He addressed me directly, pointing a threatening finger.

"Ho! I see your little game. I can guess who you are. You're that trouble-making Bolshevik union chap, aren't you?" Before I could answer he added abruptly, "Now, if there is nothing further, chaps, off you go back to your tasks. I shall be interviewing you all on an individual basis to ascertain if you are in the appropriate slot in the organisation or indeed if you will better off employed outside the waterways."

With this parting remark he dismissed us and left the building at speed.

The first skirmish was over – let the main battle commence.

There was a moment's silence before all hell broke loose, then I was bombarded with questions, complaints, threats and advice.

After arguing back and forth for a while we made a democratic decision, averting a possible strike.

I was instructed by the members to contact the personnel department, see what was going on and arrange a meeting for a week's time in the usual pub to report back. In the meanwhile I was to officially notify the manager in writing with a copy to personnel and the Union that no one would attend his assessment meetings without union and personnel representation. Craftily I added this proviso because I believed the manager was doing this off his own bat.

Mutterings of evident discontent were heard as the lads trooped back to work.

I had only been back at the lock hut for ten minutes when the telephone rang. The senior personnel manager was on the line. On recognising my voice he enquired, "What's all this about a strike? I didn't know there was any trouble over there. I thought we had an understanding that before trouble brewed we would meet and sort it out?"

I replied a bit tongue in cheek, "You never told me you were intending bringing foreigners in to take our jobs."

He exploded, "What bloody foreigners, what jobs, this is news to me? Where did this come from?"

I replied, "I can do no more than tell you that me and the lads have just left a meeting with the new manager."

I detected a kind of muffled groan on the other end of the line then his voice saying to a colleague. "I knew that bugger would be trouble the first time I laid eyes on him. Didn't I warn them at the interview?"

To me he said, "Right, I shall be over the day after tomorrow about two o'clock. Will you be there?"

I answered, "There is no point in me being there, he has made it clear he doesn't want anything to do with unions."

"Bollocks to him, Scouse, you be there. I shall be over in the morning of that day to sort things out. Do me a favour, will you? Don't let the lads do anything silly. Know what I mean?"

I replied craftily, knowing I was earning a favour, "I'll do my best but they will take some holding back. The threat of the Japanese and Germans taking their jobs has really pissed them off. Some of them were POWs in the war, you know?"

I heard another strangled groan before he put the phone down.

Things moved like clockwork after the phone call. We met at the office as arranged at two o'clock. The groundwork had already been done by the personnel department. The manager accepted union representation at the meeting although with obvious bad grace. We talked of this and that but he was still reluctant to accept the usual method of dealing with things. After about two hours of wrangling I had an adjournment to have a word with the other stewards in attendance. We considered we were making no progress and we decided to leave. When we returned to the meeting room the personnel manager persuaded us to remain. He said, "Come on, lads, have a brew and an off-the-record chat."

The manager had his super espresso machine set up and perking away. He proudly fiddled with the dials and switches, explaining the intricacies of brewing real coffee. The nut acted like a salesman! To be honest I have never liked coffee and was not interested in his demonstration. I hated tea out of vending machines so I declined the invitation for a brew. I just wanted to return to the status quo that prevailed before his appointment.

While he fussed over his machine I looked out of the window. 'Arry and Sam were cutting the grass and tidying up the garden. 'Arry spotted me and came to the outside of the window. He made gestures as if drinking, shook his head from side to side, then drew his hand across his neck. He repeated this on two or three occasions.

One of my mates, Jimmy, stood by me. I whispered, "What is 'Arry on about?"

"That's easy," he replied – having worked with 'Arry he appeared to understand the signals. He explained, "'Arry is telling us not to have a drink. I'd best warn George."

George had sat down with a steaming cup in front of him when Jim whispered the warning. The personnel department secretary and the manager's secretary joined us for the brew before the off-record chat. Unfortunately, as it turned out for them, they were all coffee lovers. I must admit that the aroma of the freshly brewed coffee was fantastic. As I watched them enjoying their first cups with relish I was tempted to try a cup myself. Fresh coffee, bacon frying, bread baking all have delicious tempting smells but due to 'Arry's warning I refrained from partaking of the coffee. At this time I had no idea why he gave us the warning so it was quite a shock when it began to happen.

I am not sure who erupted first – it could have been a duo performance by the new manager and one of the secretaries – but that was the beginning of a crescendo of musical anal expulsions. The next five minutes were hilarious. The personnel manager apologised as he farted in a rat-tat-tat machinegun-like manner. Chopper cursed and apologised alternately, emitting threatening growling noises from his posterior. The poor ladies, one squeal-farted and exited the room in haste while her companion appeared too weak to retreat and slumped in her chair sending forth farts a constipated elephant would have been proud of. She was masking her embarrassment by covering her face with her note pad. I wished they hadn't been caught up in the hostilities but in every war there are innocent victims.

Me and my two mates were helpless with laughter and supporting each other we left the room – well, you have to give a lady a shred of dignity after all.

The war was over and within a week the manager had moved on to pastures new. His replacement arrived – a long-time waterways man and a wise old bird. He knew the wonders of the waterways. We returned to the status quo, and the invasion by Japanese and Germans was again thwarted, but this time by a rabble of mostly uneducated cretins and Doctor Windbag's secret weapon.

Monday, the start of another week. The gang arrived and they were shortly joined by a newcomer, a huge red-faced Irishman. He was not of the regular workforce and had been engaged to operate a high pressure water pump to clear lime blockages in the ancient turbine feeds. His boss, the contractor, introduced him with a sneer as 'Fetchit' but we soon learned his real name was surprisingly 'Paddy Lopez'.

"Take no notice of dat gob shite," Paddy informed us after he left. "Just 'cos I was a messenger boy in his village he tinks it's funny to call me dat name. One of dese days I'll thump de bleeder but Oye need de job at de minute."

The machine he was operating was considered too dangerous for our lads to use. The first thing he did when he set it up and cranked up the mighty diesel engine was demonstrate the power of the jet by cutting a rubber tyre through and splintering a railway sleeper. Paddy explained he always did this before getting down to the allotted tasks so his workmates would stay clear of the deadly instrument. Needless to say he didn't have to warn our lads twice when they witnessed his awesome demonstration.

Baggin time came as usual and the lads trooped into the hut. Brickie had been doing his usual weekend hobby of scouring the car boot sales for bargains. On this occasion he had purchased a number of smart-looking leather-bound books. The one he was currently reading was entitled *The Wonders of the Modern and Ancient World*. The books fascinated 'Arry and the other lads as Brickie read extracts to them and showed the pictures.

Paddy entered the hut just as Brickie arrived at the chapter describing Hadrian's Wall. As he sat down he exclaimed, "Ah, so dis is where you all is. I wondered where'd you'd gone. Oive never seen fellas disappear so fast as youse lot!"

He sat quietly for a moment then asked, "And where is that then, that place you was on about?"

Brickie explained, "Oh sorry, Paddy, you missed it. The wall is stretched across Britain and separates Scotland and England."

Paddy thought for a moment before questioning, "I have been to Scotland a few times and never seen a wall across the way. Who built that, then, you say?"

Brickie explained, "Big chunks of it are missing, that's why you missed seeing it. Hadrian built it."

Paddy asked, "Is he a contractor or what? I've worked for all the big 'uns and never heard of that outfit."

Brickie answered in an amazed voice, "No, he's not – or should I say wasn't – a contractor, you daft bugger, he was a Roman Emperor."

Paddy a little miffed, warned Brickie, "I wud dank you not to call me a daft bugger, all right?"

Brickie, taken aback by his threatening manner, replied, "Sorry, Paddy, I meant no harm. It's the way we talk to each other around here, it's not serious."

Paddy nodded, accepted his apology and asked, "What's a Roman when he's about, where is he from then?"

"I suppose you could say he will be an Italian," Brickie explained. 'Arry interceded indignantly.

"What the bloody hell have we got Italian contractors over here doing our jobs, that's not right? I bet half the buggers are on the lump and don't pay any tax or insurance."

"Common Market. I bet that's what that's all about. You know we could go to Roman and work there if we wanted same as they can come here," Jacko gave us the benefit of his knowledge.

"Do they pay double on a weekend?" Abba enquired then quickly added, "I wouldn't mind working in some other country, it would get me away from my bleedin' in-laws, but I've heard they eat all kinds of weird things." Abba visibly shuddered with horror. His daily diet didn't vary much and certainly didn't include anything he considered un-English.

This was getting to be a good debate. I chipped in my two-penneth to stir things up a bit more, despite Brickie trying to bring them back to the subject of the Roman Conquest of Britain. He gave me a dirty look when I offered further information for the benefit of the assembled lads.

"They were Roman soldiers that built the wall, lads. They built roads and forts all over the place. Bath houses, mansions, whorehouses, palaces for the rich. They were great builders, the Old Roman lads."

'Arry replied in an unbelieving manner, "When was that then? I haven't heard about it. Why didn't our own army build the wall, why bring foreigners in to do the job?"

I could see Brickie getting frustrated. He snorted in disgust. Poor old Brickie didn't appreciate the value of these debates; he liked to stick strictly to the facts.

"You daft bugger, 'Arry, it was hundreds of years ago; don't you know your history? If you lot would let me finish this story it would have explained everything. "

'Arry went into a sulk when his lack of education was highlighted. Abba saw his chance and asked the question again. "Well, is anyone going to tell me? Do they pay double time on a Sunday or what?"

Typical of Abba. That's how he acquired his nickname from the pop group's name and the song "Money, money, money". Abba is always broke; his in-laws take everything he earns off him.

I felt the need to offer some words of wisdom. Very coincidentally, only the previous night I had been watching a panel game on TV and learnt an interesting fact. I now had the opportunity to use it in a smug knowledgeable manner.

"Well, Abba, my old lad, you might not believe this but the Roman soldiers didn't get paid in cash. They got salt. I don't think they got double salt on a Sunday though, as they were pagans. Sunday wasn't a holy day so no dubs, I'm afraid."

'Arry exploded, "Daft I call it, whoever heard of not having Sundays and if Pontius tried to give me a bag of salt on payday I'd stick it up his arse."

Amongst the laughter 'Arry dropped his voice and in a serious manner told us, "Hey lads, best keep this to us in case the bosses hear of it. You know what them buggers are like – anything to save a few bob!"

I added another gem of wisdom I had read about.

"Hey 'Arry, and them Romans used vinegar to cure all kinds of things. So when you next go in the chippy and they put salt and vinegar on the chips there is your wages and your National Health all in one."

'Arry gave a toothless grin and said, "You daft bugger, Scouse, you don't half come up with some crap at times."

Brickie intervened and imparted, "It's true about the vinegar, 'Arry, you should know that being a bit of a medic yourself."

'Arry replied thoughtfully, "I have used it on bee stings and I use salt to cure cuts and scrapes – it's all right for burns as well, but I will try vinegar myself in future to see what happens."

Paul said nervously, "You needn't think you are trying it on me 'Arry. Find another victim for your medical experiments. I remember what you did to that carbuncle on my neck, you cruel sod."

'Arry laughed and replied, "It cured you, Paul, you moanin' bugger."

Big Al seriously offered his explanation. Being an Italian he considered himself an expert on Roman history. His stature appeared to increase as he took credit for his ancestors and explained, "You see, 'Arry, my lot, by that I mean us Italians, because years ago the Italians was called Romans..."

'Arry interrupted, "Why was you called Romins if you was I-ties?"

Al explained patiently, "Because, 'Arry, we was from a place name of Rome. For your further information, it was called after two wolves called Romulus and Remus."

'Arry thought for a moment before enquiring. "Well why wasn't you called Remusuns? And what daft buggers calls themselves after an animal?"

"I reckon Congleton did," Paul who had been listening to the debate intently offered. He added with uncertainty. "But I suppose that was after a kind of fish, if a Conger eel is a fish? And the Irish was called after a dog as well."

Jacko asked with a sneer, "What dog were the Irish called after?"

Paul replied triumphantly, "Irish Bloody Wolfhound, smart arse."

I grinned and congratulated him. It's not often Paul wins a point off Jacko.

"One up for you Paul, nice one."

It appeared that Paddy liked that one as well as he gave a deep chuckle.

Big Al bravely ignored the interruptions and carried on with enthusiasm.

"But we didn't speak Italian then, we spoke what's known as

Latin. We ruled all the known world at one time. We conquered all of Europe and big chunks of Africa with the Roman Legions and lots of chariots. In fact you could say without contradiction we was the top dogs for years all over the place. Anyone gave us a bit of lip, mate, and we sent our Legions in and kicked their arse, I can tell you. What we did have was problems with the Mad Jocks with their ugly faces painted all blue. You know what they are like when they get pissed? Anyway we gave up on trying to civilise the mad buggers so we built this wall across to keep them out. The name of the wall was called after the Roman Emperor of the time and he was called Hadrian."

Jacko exclaimed, "Don't be giving us a load of cobblers, Al. The I'ties couldn't fight their way out of a paper bag. As soon as Monty and the Desert Rats turned up you lot threw the towel in."

He snorted contemptuously and added, "Conquered all the known world? Do us a favour! And for your language information, only Doctors and Professors speak Latin."

Paddy gave a kind of gruff growl and added, "Ain't youse forgetten someone's important. Youse forget the Priests and de Pope. Oi believe day speaks in Latin."

Al sheepishly continued explaining about the Romans, his moment of glory drained away by Jacko's reminder of the last war.

"I know about the Latin and them that still speaks it, but to everyone else it's what's known as a dead language. I'm not thick, you know. Well, you lot better believe what I said about the Roman Army. I will admit we was rubbish in World War Two 'cos we didn't want to fight. We hated the Fascist sod Mussolini and I was forced to join his stupid bloody army and sent to a shit hole country called Ethiopia. The British did the same to their lads, you know. Any of you lot been in the army?"

Brickie and I put our hands up. I saw the opportunity to cause a bit of chaos and remarked, "I was in the army but I wasn't sent to Ethiopia though, Al. Sounds a good posting. Women were nice there, were they?"

Al disdainfully ignored my information and enquired, "Was you volunteers, I mean did you have a choice?"

We both revealed we only did compulsory national service. Triumphantly Al informed us, "There you are then, none of us had any choice."

I added, "Except the regulars, of course, they wasn't forced to go. I bet there was plenty in the Italian army, Al, same as ours."

Paddy who had been quiet for a while said, "I did, cos I refused to go in the army, so I had a choice."

This information disrupted poor Al's flow yet again but he soon recovered and pointed out, "Ah! But Paddy, that's because you are Irish and the Irish don't have to go into the British army if they don't want to."

Paddy replied with a grim look on his face. "Me dad did, and mo brother did, so did me cousin, and two of me uncles."

Jacko questioned him, "I don't get it. Why did they do that then, Paddy, if they didn't have to?" He added with conviction, "You wouldn't get me in a bloody army, no way."

Paddy informed us, "They wanted to learn to drive trucks. The recruiting sergeant promised them if they signed on he would personally see they learnt to drive."

Jacko replied, "Well, that's not so bad then, they got something out of it."

Paddy said, "He was a liar, the Protestant swine of Hell. They all finished up in Burma with an outfit called the Chindits driving bloody mules with the Japanese shooting at them all the time. They were doing exactly what they did before joining up but they was driving donkeys in Ireland and there was no Japanese shooting at them."

On a totally different vein he added, "Did you lot know they don't have spuds in Burma, only rice? That's what really pissed me dad off."

Defeated Al moved on, determined to get his point over before the end of baggin time. "Anyway now that is cleared up back to the past. The Roman army was brilliant and it is true about us ruling the known world 'cos it's written down in history books, even in yours."

'Arry interceded, "If them Romin fellas only ruled the known world who ruled the unknown one?"

Al, frustrated by the interruptions, exploded, "Bloody hell, 'Arry! How am I supposed to know that, it was unknown? I am not going to try answering that one."

He appealed to Brickie, the fund of all knowledge and the settler of many arguments.

"Is that right, Brickie, about the Romans ruling the..." he looked pointedly at 'Arry, adding. "...and I stress, the *known* world?"

Brickie confirmed the facts.

"Is that right, Scouse?" he appealed to me to confirm Brickie's confirmation.

"You're right, Al, they was at one time the greatest army in the world until the Vandals gave them grief and they had to withdraw back to Rome but that's another story."

Al, sensing triumph, continued, "You lot must have heard of Julius Caesar, Anthony and Cleopatra, Brutus and all those other Emperors?"

'Arry's face lit up. "Yes, I saw the picture about her on the local flea pit, she done herself in with a snake at the end. Pity really, she was a tasty piece."

Being an avid picturegoer due to his back row liaison with a cinema usherette, Paul joined in the debate for the first time. Paul is a good lad but everyone knows he is two pence short of a bob and has some peculiar ideas.

"That wasn't really Cleopatra, 'Arry, it was an actress."

'Arry rebuked him with scorn.

"I know that, you daft bugger, they wouldn't let a real actress be bit by a snake. It was most probably someone who was dying anyway and they paid her to stand in."

'Arry searched in his big holdall, extracted a paper bag, handed it to Paul and advised, "Sit there quietly Paul. Eat your nuts, you know they are good for the brain. Being with the likes of us will improve your education, listening to those that knows."

Without protest Paul obeyed him, took the bag and began consuming the contents.

'Arry divulged another fact about Cleopatra. "Eh, you know what, she used to get in a bath full of asses' milk. I don't know what a bloody ass is but she definitely got into a bath full of the stuff. It was in the picture, you never got to see her tits, though – the milk came right up to her neck. What about that then?" he announced the fact proudly.

"What was that all about?" Paddy asked. "Why would she get into a bath of milk? Surely it would make you stink worse, especially in the summer. Ain't she got no running water in her place?"

'Arry enlightened him. "You daft bugger, Paddy, course they had no running water – it was in a foreign country."

Paddy stood up and warned, "Now lads, let's get this straight once and for all. I don't like being called a daft bugger, if anyone else calls me dat we is going to fall out, get it?"

I interceded. Paddy looked in a dangerous mood and I couldn't have any violence in my lock hut.

"Now then, Paddy, calm yourself down This is my lock hut and you are all guests in here. These lads meet here regular and we don't have no trouble. You are welcome to join us while you work here but you must understand. The debates in here are a free for all and anyone can say what they like except we don't discuss religion. When someone calls another a name it is just an expression and means no harm. That's the rules, Paddy, my friend, like 'em or lump 'em."

He stood towering over me, then stuck out his huge hand and shook mine. He apologised, "Sorry, lads, it's just dat boss of mine keeps a calling me dat and it pisses me off. OK if I stay? I loiks de company and de talk about knowledgeable tings."

I gestured him to take his seat.

"Egypt. That's where Anthony was goosing Cleopatra." Abba declared, breaking the silence. "They don't have things like us in foreign countries."

'Arry ridiculed his statement.

"How do you know you daft bugger, you have only been as far as Blackpool in your whole life."

Abba replied indignantly. "I met a fella down the pub. You know him, he perches at the end of the bar, drinks nothing but black rum? He's got a beard and tattoos – he's an old sailor and had been all over the world. We was talking about foreign places one night and he told me they don't have proper bogs like us.

They just have a hole in the floor and stand up to do the business."

His statement brought silence as they contemplated the revelation. After a moment Brickie revealed, "Well, for your information I know that guy you are on about, he was on the mud hoppers on the Ship Canal all his life, you silly sod, Abba. Incidentally the Romans did have running water and sit-down bogs when they was over here. I can tell you 'cos I have seen them. I went to see one of the forts on Hadrian's Wall last year on my holidays and they have all kinds of things that would surprise you lot. They even had central heating in their houses."

'Arry remarked incredulously, repeating it twice. "Central bloody heating! Central bloody heating! We haven't even got that now in our place. Cissie is always on about it, nesh bugger she is – wants to sit around in a frock in winter, that's what she wants to do. Put another bloody coat on, I tells her when she moans about the cold. Bloody expensive, that central heating. I burn all the wood we get out of the cut meself, much cheaper. That's her excuse for going over to the boozer 'cos they got central heating in there. She says she only goes for a warm. Warm my arse, she gets pissed!"

Abba chipped in, "Hey, 'Arry, what's her excuse in the summer then? Ha, ha! It would be cheaper having central heating and air conditioning put in your place than keeping your missus in booze. She can't half shift it. As for surviving on the wood out of the cut, you conveniently forgot to mention the coal that falls off passing boats and finishes up in your fire. Miracle that, eh, lads! Ha, ha!"

Hoots of laughter greeted his remark. 'Arry gave him a withering glare. Brickie ignored the latest 'Arry and Abba deviation and informed us. "The only weird thing was they had no bog paper as such. The guide that showed us around explained they used a stick with a sponge on to wipe their arses."

Paddy was incredulous at this bit of information. "A stick with a sponge on? A sponge on de end of a stick? What's dat all about den, didn't they have dock leaves like we used in de old country?"

Brickie looked at the newcomer with disdain, unable to believe we had been joined by another head case. I think when he saw

Paddy he was hoping for someone more intelligent to have sensible debates with. He asked, "Where are you from, Paddy? I know you sound like a Mick but I have never heard of a Mick named Lopez."

"Dat's a long story, matey," Paddy replied. "I am indeed from Old Ireland that's for sure but bejasus, dat was a long, long time ago. You had these fellas called Drake and Nelson, they was Admirals with your navy. Did you know them?"

"Well, not personally," Brickie replied nervously. "But I have heard of them, I am not sure if they were around at the same time."

Paddy made a kind of disapproving noise in his throat. Hurriedly Brickie said, "Anyway, never mind that, what's that to do with anything?"

"Sure if I'm not comin' to dat if you'll give me the chance. Have any of you lot heard of the Spanish armada?"

A few of the lads nodded, others sat silent trying not to show their ignorance. Paddy explained, "You see der was dis big battle at a place called Trafalgar between the Spanish and English navies. And the Spanish got a right tousin."

'Arry butted in, "Why was they fightin the Spanish? Seems funny to me, lots of people are going there for their holidays! I seen it on the pictures."

Paddy explained patiently. "It was a long time ago, 'Arry. The Spanish was going to invade England."

"What for?" 'Arry asked. "The Germans tried that and got their arse kicked. We showed the buggers. Ha, ha. I know that's true 'cos it was in my time. Old Churchill sure rammed his fat cigar up crazy Adolph's arse, eh, lads?"

His remarks were greeted by victorious cheers until they were interrupted by Abba.

"Don't forget Napoleon! We kicked his arse as well," Abba exclaimed and began singing the patriotic song, "Land of hope is our men."

Brickie told him, "Shut up, Abba, you noisy bugger. Anyway you have got the words of the song mixed up. If you must sing those stupid songs at least get the words right. Paddy, you was telling us why the Spanish was going to invade us, go on – we'll have to get back to work in a minute. Pontius is coming down some time today to see your squirter thing operating."

"To make all you lot true God-fearing Catholic Christians," Paddy informed him as he stood up and left the hut.

One by one the lads trooped out to start work. Brickie whispered to me, "We'll have to watch this one, Scouse, I think he is a bit of a nutcase. What was that business all about the Spanish armada? Nelson and Drake were years apart – they were two different sea battles. Eh! And another thing, Scouse, have you noticed the way this Paddy speaks? One minute he is talking like a thick bog Mick and the next thing he is all posh-like. There's something fishy about this character, I can tell you."

I retorted, "I have no idea, Brickie, mate, maybe he will finish his story at Mungano time, eh?"

(We called it 'Mungano time', it was really the lunch break and originated from the Scouse word 'mungie' as in "Gorra get me Mungie, I'm bleedin' starvin.'" Then Big Al, the Italian POW, arrived and learned to speak Scouse. It was only one step to stick 'ano' on the end of the word as some of our continental neighbours are inclined to do...)

Brickie answered, "I hope so and another thing, he touched on religion, that's not allowed. Scouse, you should tell him we don't have none of that in here."

Indignantly I replied, "I've told him once but I'll mention it again if he broaches it, OK? If you want to warn him yourself, feel free."

Brickie left, muttering.

Puddling Paul hung back and when the others were out of earshot he asked, "Hey, Scouse, you know them Vandals you was on about?"

I replied hesitantly, wondering where this was leading.

"Yes, what about them?"

Paul asked, "Are those the ones that do all that scribbling on the walls and smash up the telephone boxes?"

I paused before replying, considering my answer thoughtfully.

"Hmmm! Difficult one to answer, Paul, my old mate. You see

there was a mob in Europe years ago that destroyed everything in their path and caused chaos everywhere they went. The name came from them, so anyone that does damage and causes problems these days they call them Vandals. Why do you ask?"

Paul replied, "Well, I was just wondering, if those Roman fellas you was on about had telephones in those days. That's all. Thanks, Scouse, I understand now, and I was going to tell Jacko 'Labradors' instead of 'Irish Wolf Hounds', but he wouldn't know where that was, he's an ignorant bugger."

I replied, "I am glad you understand that, Paul. Now can you explain something to me? Why does 'Arry give you a bag of nuts now and again? It's not like 'Arry to give anything away. I've never seen you pay him."

Paul replied, "That's easy, Scouse, he doesn't give 'em to me free like, they are my nuts anyway. 'Arry being a medic tells me they are good for the brain so I buys a load of 'em on Saturday from the market and gives em to 'Arry. He gives 'em back to me so many at a time in doses like. I reckon its working 'cos I am getting really knowledgeable about all kinds of things."

I have to admit that I have read somewhere that consuming Brazil nuts is supposed to improve intelligence and memory. Paul's contributions to the debates were definitely improving as he divulged some interesting facts. Sometimes they were not relevant to the subject being debated, but nevertheless? Maybe 'Arry was right with his nutty medication after all.

The lad's reasoning, however, still puzzled me. I shouldn't have been surprised really, I was dealing with Paul, after all. I enquired, "But why don't you just space them out and eat so many each day?"

"Hmmm! That's easy as well, Scouse. I don't like the chocolate on 'em. I'm not one for sweet things."

Paul left the hut whistling a happy tune. The way this lad's mind worked was a wonder to me. When I tackled 'Arry later about it he grinned and revealed, "Don't tell Paul, but me and Cissie loves the chocolate on 'em. We got a taste for it years ago when we did the crumb run on the boats to Cadburys. Me and Cissie having no teeth we can't cope with the nuts. So to do Paul a favour we sucks all the chocolate off and I gives 'em back to him a bag at a time."

When I protested in horror and enquired, "Why doesn't Paul just buy the plain nuts?" he informed me, "Now then, Scouse! My nut treatment is improving Paul's brain and I gets my medical fee in chocolate. You shouldn't question things you don't understand."

Paddy's warning was enough to keep our lads well clear when he began his operation. As the locks were closed to shipping due to the repairs, having nothing better to do I stood at a safe distance watching Paddy performing. It was indeed a fearsome machine – at the end of the long flexible pipe attached to the massive pump was a lance with a trigger device. This he replaced with a special mushroom-shaped adaption with holes facing both ways. This concentrated the flow of high pressure water to needle thin jets that forced the adaption into the completely blocked feeder pipes, scouring and clearing them as it passed along the 18-inch cast iron tube. The heavily lime and scale-laden near-boiling water was fired out of the turbine exhaust. Every now and again Paddy stopped the operation, giving our lads time to clear away the residue. It was at those times that Paddy disclosed some details of his life. But first he had to establish a fact.

When he stopped the operation I enquired, "How did you get involved with this machine, Paddy? It's quite an invention and very technical-looking."

Instead of Paddy answering my question he replied with a startling query, "Are you a company spy keeping an eye on me?"

"Me a company spy?" I laughed nervously. "I'm the union rep, Paddy, the last thing I am is a company spy. Why would you think that?"

He explained, "Cos you are the only one doin' nothing."

I replied with another laugh, "Oh, I understand now. That's because the locks are closed for repairs. My job is to operate them. No, I'm just interested in your machine, Paddy."

"Right den oi'll answer your question. Der was a fella in our village in Ireland, me old Dad knew him well. He went to America and did well for his self, operating a machine loike dis one clearing out oil pipes and de like. Anyway he won some money at a gambling place called Las Vegas. He took a chance, bought one of the machines and had it shipped over to England. He was getting a bit old and he took me on and learned me all about it. I have been working it for a couple of years. Dis is not the original machine, it's the latest updated version. The company is planning to get some more if they can train de operators. I travel all over de place doing jobs with it."

I asked, "Then who was that fella that brought you here, he doesn't look that old? I reckon you don't like him much, is that right?"

"Dat man McCriethy is his son-in-law. The old fella I told you about has had a stroke so this bugger is running the company now and he is a right shit. I am tempted to punch his lights out every toime I sees him. He wants me out and he is trying to get me to jack in and he can work one of his latchico's in. He knows he can't just sack me, the old man wudn't have it, but I have dis plan you see." Paddy tapped the side of his nose. "I just have to do this job and I have enough to get to America, 'cos I have been offered a good job over there demonstrating dese machines for dem. Then McCriethy can shove his machine up his arse. Well, I see de lads have cleared de muck, so back to work we go."

There was much rustling of paper bags and the snap of plastic butty boxes as the lads got stuck into their food. Gradually a hush came over the lock hut as the lads observed Paddy preparing his enormous sandwich. He took a whole unsliced loaf, and ripped it in two parts long ways. He opened a packet of margarine and rubbed it thickly over the both pieces of bread. In between he stuffed two huge meat and potato pies which he crushed flat; a packet of crisps was added, then half a jar of pickled onions. On top of this he poured a huge blob of brown sauce. He squeezed the lot together and commenced eating. Having completed this lot he pulled a full-sized homemade apple pie from his bag and consumed the lot, washed down with a couple of bottles of Guinness.

The lads, particularly 'Arry, were overcome with admiration. 'Arry asked when he had finished, "Good chuck, eh, Paddy? Your missus looks after you all right, eh?"

"Ain't married, never have been and never will be," Paddy

informed him briefly.

"Who puts your chuck up, then, Paddy? I could do with someone like that meself," 'Arry moaned. "My missus is always trying to cut me back on rations."

Paddy explained, "Landlady looks after me. I haven't got anywhere permanent to live. I just move around from lodging to lodging wherever the jobs are. Had a caravan once and dragged it from job to job with my van but I got lonely especially at night. When I got fed up eating fish and chips all the time I decided to live in digs. Always seem to find good landladies that look after me real well. They looks after my needs, and I looks after their needs. Know what I mean?" he winked at 'Arry.

'Arry responded with a whisper of admiration, "You lucky bugger, Paddy. I knows exactly what you mean. When I was single on the trade boats travelling around the country there was many a tasty bird that needed plucking and appreciated the service us boat lads provided."

He licked his lips and added in a lecherous way, "Especially in the war when there was a shortage of fellas. Mind you when the Yanks came over they buggered that up, I can tell you."

The idea of 'Arry as a roaming sex machine satisfying the man-starved women of Britain made me shudder. The women must have been real desperate years ago.

Brickie interceded – he didn't like such talk, it appeared to embarrass him. He said, "Now then, Paddy, you was explaining about your name and the Spanish armada this morning at baggin. Will you finish the story or should I go onto the next wondrous thing in the book? It's about the Hanging Gardens of Babylon."

Paddy wiped his mouth on his sleeve and replied, "Not much more to tell really. According to the nun that taught us history at school your English navy scattered the Spanish armada 'cos their sailors were all sick with the plague and couldn't fight proper like. They tried to get back to Spain but there was a big storm and some of them finished up wrecked on the Irish coast. Them Spanish fellas being good Catholics and the Irish being good Catholics and them both hatin' the English Proddies, they got on well together. Some of the Spanish lads married some of the Irish girls and that's how my name is Lopez. That's why I look sunburned all the time even in winter when there is no sun, it's the Spanish blood in me."

Abba remarked in a surprised manner, "I wondered why your face was so red, Paddy. I thought you just had blood pressure like my old man. Well I never, sunburnt!"

Brickie hurriedly moved things on when he noticed the change in Paddy's expression when Abba stated this.

"Oh, I see, one of your ancestors was a Spanish sailor? That accounts for the swarthy skin and name, eh? Bloody good, er, interesting story, Paddy. I heard of the same thing happening in Scotland as well. There are lots of dark-skinned Scots people especially on the East coast where some of the galleons got wrecked. The Spanish survivors were safe in Scotland because they was Catholic as well and didn't like the English much either."

Paddy answered, "I wouldn't be surprised, not many people liked youse lot years ago, did they? Youse was always causin' trouble, shooting poor buggers and robbin' their land off them. There was another thing de old nun told us. Youse lot never won all de battles. No sir, you sure did not. There was that Viking lot, they came over to your place regular and robbed all your gear and shagged all your women. They used to live in Dublin, you know? I bet you never knew that one, eh?"

Brickie replied smugly, "Well, I did, as a matter of fact. They also lived on the Isle of Man. They reckon their descendants have red hair."

Paddy ignored him and continued, "Then der was William the Conkerer. You don't mention him and de way him and his Frenchies walked all over your lot much, do you?"

I felt the need to move on when I observed our lads getting slightly uncomfortable as Paddy revealed fact after fact about our history that they were evidently ignorant about. By relating a little known morsel I had recently discovered, I made a stand for England and remarked, "Nice one, Paddy, you sure know your history. But let's not slag the English all the time. Seeing as you know your history, what about all the Irish fellas that went to America and joined the Seventh Cavalry? Then with General Custer and his load of butchers they went about slaughtering the native Indians, women and children included, just to steal their land."

Paddy replied sullenly, "I never heard about that. OK, most people in history had innocent blood on their hands. Oyl give you dat, Scouse."

We needed to lighten up the debate, this subject was getting too serious and Paddy was looking slightly aggressive. I was sorry I'd mentioned the Seventh Cavalry but facts are facts and all's fair in love and the Great Lock Hut Debates. This was what I told myself, anyway. Thankfully 'Arry helped me out when he introduced a completely fresh subject.

"Talking of boats sinking? Tell 'em your pension idea, Scouse, it's great."

I replied reluctantly, "Ah, eh, 'Arry, it was only a joke, not to be taken seriously."

"What's all this then, Scouse? You keeping something from us? Come on, tell all!" Brickie enquired. The rest of the lads joined in trying to persuade me to reveal the nonsense. I tried to explain.

"It was just some thing I said at the pre-retirement seminars, you know just to get things going in those debates I hold of an evening."

'Arry gleefully protested, "Just a joke or not! In my opinion it's a bloody good idea and me and Cissie will be signing up for it when we finish work, I can tell you."

I retorted, trying to make light of it, "'Arry, it won't happen believe me. For Jesus' sake, I'm sorry I mentioned it."

Brickie saw I was in the shit and pushed me further in by saying, "Too late, Scouse, you've already said it and we want to know. If it affects our pension fund we are entitled to know. In case you forgot you are elected by us to look after our interests. We don't want any secrets, do we lads?"

Roars of disapproval greeted his remarks.

"All right, but you must understand it is not official pension fund policy."

Sarcastically, I agreed to reveal what I said at the pension seminar that 'Arry and his wife had previously attended.

"It's a bit complicated but it goes like this. You know the miners are out of work because of the government's policy?"

The lads agreed, we had backed the miners in the strike and the lads were sympathetic.

"You know the steel workers are short of work because of foreign imports?"

"Yes," was the reply from the lads in unison.

"You know the shipyards are closing because the lousy ship owners are ordering their ships from abroad? We talked about all these things at the union meetings and how we could help our fellow workers by buying British?"

"Yes."

"You know the old people's homes and hospitals are full of old people having a miserable life. Other poor buggers are in their own homes living alone, freezing cold half the time because they can't afford to heat them because the lousy government privatised the electric companies?"

"Yes."

Abba urged me on, "Come on, Scouse, get to the nitty gritty. Mungano time is nearly up."

I continued after his interruption, which the other lads condemned noisily.

"Well, my idea is this. You know if there is a war the government always finds money to build ships and other instruments of war, for example in the Falklands conflict with the Argies?"

The responses of 'yes' were not so positive to this question. Undaunted I carried on.

"Well, as there is no war now, instead they should use the money that they would have found if there was a war. Do you follow me so far?"

I recognised looks of bewilderment but continued anyway.

"Right, I can see you lot understand. With the money they save by not having a war the government pays to build loads of cruise ships. They have to be powered by steam not diesel or oil, you know – coal burners just like the old days? This is a crucial part of the plan because it will give our miners work and there is another reason but that will become clear later on.

"The steel workers and the shipyard workers will be all right as well, with plenty of orders to keep 'em off the dole.

"Then we round up all the retired seamen who spend their old age in pubs and clubs telling everyone what a great life they had at sea shagging their way around the world...

"All right so far?"

"Yes."

"Now we are getting to the crux of the plan. We gets all the old people and puts them on these ships and they sail off to the sunshine away from the shitty winter. They are having a great time with free booze, Viagra tablets and food and vitamins. The food is well mushed up so they can digest it easy and slurp it without their teeth in. No one will moan if they dribble and spill it on the deck. I have even thought of an answer to that one. You have seen them sprinklers that come on if there is a fire in a hotel?"

"Yes."

"Well, here is the idea. Even though I say myself I think it's brilliant. After the old ones have finished their meals we turn them sprinklers on. This will save them having to get washed and it will clean the ship down at the same time – good one, eh?"

I waited for approval but it didn't come so I moved on quickly.

"Now to keep them amused they have lots of bingo and zimmer races, so they would be as happy as Larry, you reckon?"

"Yes, good idea, Scouse. Why don't the bloody government do it then, the tight sods?" Abba protested angrily.

Brickie put a damper on the idea by stating, "Because it would be too expensive. You couldn't keep circling the oceans with ships full of old people. What about when they died? They would have to keep bringing the bodies home for burial – that would cost a fortune."

Jacko objected, "No, it wouldn't be too expensive – we could all give up our pensions and that ten pounds Christmas bonus the tight buggers pay us. And the winter heating allowance could buy the coal for the engines."

Abba interrupted, "Don't forget what a funeral costs with the Co-op nowadays. I heard it cost thousands of pounds to get buried decent-like these days."

Abba revealed another fact about his family. "Me granddad had to take out a loan to bury me granny – she wanted one of those big marble angels over her grave. He was supposed to leave me some money when he died but all he left was a debt due to that stupid bloody angel. This is what really pisses me off, there was no room in the grave for him when he popped his clogs soon after me granny. The bloody grave was full of me in-laws. The tight buggers wouldn't buy their own grave and snook into ours. I nearly had to buy a new one until I heard the University was taking dead bodies and burying them free after they cut 'em up a bit for the students. No, Scouse, this is a good idea and I want you to bring it up at the next pension meeting in London. I think they should just dump the dead bodies over the side with a flag over them and the Captain saying a bit of a prayer."

Paul congratulated him, "Nice one, Abba, just like they do in those Navy pictures. I wouldn't mind that meself as long as I was dead and the water was warm with no jellyfish. I mean I can't swim, I don't like getting in a cold bath and I got stung by a jellyfish in Blackpool when I was a kid. It didn't half hurt."

'Arry sniggered, "You daft bugger, Paul, why are you worrying about swimming and cold water and jellyfish – you'll be dead, anyway!"

Paul shrank into his corner.

Al had an idea and entered the debate.

"That money they give normally to the grabbing undertakers will help to pay for the cruise. It will save cemetery space as well as feeding the fishes."

Jacko enthusiastically offered his ideas, "And don't forget them crematoriums polluting the atmosphere with the fumes off the dead bodies. It will be what the scientist blokes on the telly like call very 'environmentally friendly'. It's a wonder Greenpeace hasn't thought of it before now."

The debate was getting heated when 'Arry interceded, "Scouse hasn't finished yet. Tell 'em the best part, Scouse."

I protested as everyone seemed to be happy so far with my ideas. "Ah no, 'Arry, that was just another daft idea."

Brickie again came to my rescue (I don't think).

"We want to know all the details, Scouse, no leaving bits out, come on."

I replied reluctantly, "Right here goes. Well, the pensioners are having this great time pissed every night on the free booze and as much marihuana they can stuff in their pipes. They are all nice and warm 'cos the ship only cruises in hot places like the Caribbean."

As I revealed my plan I began to get enthusiastic and embellished the idea.

"Picture the scene – they are sitting around on their commodes just before bedtime about eight o'clock…"

"What's a commode, Scouse?" Paul asked. I replied impatiently, "Oh, bloody hell, Paul, you are spoiling my flow. A commode is a portable bog. Anyway…"

I was about to continue when Paul interrupted again.

"Why would they be sitting around on portable bogs? Men and women, in front of each other on bogs! I don't fancy that, Scouse, I like a bit of privacy on the bog. Leave me out of that one."

Thankfully 'Arry rescued me, "Bloody hell, Paul, think of it. You would normally have to get up to go to the bog. If we use Scouse's idea you could just eat and drink and do the business without moving from the bar. It sounds like a brilliant idea to me. Carry on, Scouse, if he doesn't want to come leave the miserable bugger out when we sail on the cruise. Let him stay at home sitting on his own bog by hiself."

Thanking 'Arry for his intervention I continued.

"Where was I? Oh! Yes. The old ones have had another brilliant day watching Max Bygraves and Bruce Forsyth performing. Margaret Thatcher has come out especially on her private helicopter." I confided as if I was privy to a secret. "She paid for the helicopter out of the money she made flogging off the mental hospitals to her mates."

"What's she want with us? I'm not coming if she's there," Abba retorted angrily.

I responded tolerantly. "Don't worry Abba, it will turn out right in the end, be patient. She has come to be with the old folks as she is taking credit for the whole old people's cruising idea even although it is all mine. You know what politicians and bosses are like for stealing other people's ideas? Anyway, she is trying to make a comeback with her new political party."

"Oh no, not another gang of quacking politicians jamming up the telly at election time?" 'Arry moaned.

I replied in a regretful voice, "Yes, I am sorry, 'Arry, but her mind is made up, you know what a stubborn cow she can be. Anyway her new party – it's going to be called er? Er? The Incontinence Unionists. She is trying to get grey power to vote for her. The slogan of her new party at the next election is to be ... 'Shit or Bust'."

Paul said, "Well she needn't think she is getting my vote. I thought we had seen the last of her!"

'Arry interceded again, "This is the part I like best. Go on, Scouse, make 'em have it."

A little bit lamely I revealed the final part of my master plan.

"Then without warning the ship is blown to smithereens and sinks to the bottom of the sea. Everyone is blown to kingdom come."

Except for 'Arry's chuckle, silence greeted my last statement.

To lighten the atmosphere up, I added, "Don't look too glum, lads, there is a happy side to all this. The Army has got rid of its past sell-by-date explosives. The fishes have a good feed off the bits of bodies. The wreck of the ship becomes an artificial reef. There is no pollution because she only has coal on. No oil, you see, to float all over the place."

Proudly I added, "See lads, I thought of everything. Anyway the shipyard gets another order for a pensioners' cruise ship. The steel workers and miners are happy as pigs in shit. The hospital waiting lists have been cut. The nurses and doctors spend their days screwing each other in the empty beds like they do on the telly. Those scheming swine that ran the old people's homes go bankrupt. The unemployed undertakers can get jobs in the mines or the shipyards. The surplus funeral cars can be used as taxis to pick up and deliver the old people to the cruise ship. The hearses can have a mattress in the back to take you home pissed. You can have a sleep on the way or a bit of the other in the back where the coffins used to be.

"When she is dead, Dear Margaret will have to tell the truth to the lads she had killed on the *General Belgrano* down in the Falklands. That's supposing she goes to the same place as the Argentine sailors, which I very much doubt. I think they have a special place reserved for politicians when they pop their clogs."

"Where's that then, Scouse?" Paul asks.

I reply cynically. "I'm not sure, Paul, you see no one will tell them where they are. It will be covered by the Official Secrets Act and can't be disclosed for a hundred years. But I guarantee this, it will certainly be full of liars promising all kinds and doing nowt except scheming and plotting and fiddling their expenses. Hey! And I have just thought of this, there won't be a state funeral for Margaret. No body to bury, see. That will be another big saving and the money can go towards paying for the free booze on the cruise!"

This is getting better the more I think of it.

"We won't have to watch Max Bygraves again singing those awful bloody songs. He can go and entertain that thieving sod Maxwell that stole the newspaper lads' pensions. But the best of all we won't see that boring old fart Bruce Forsyth on the telly any more."

Roars of approval welcomed my last remark,

"And he can stuff his drip dry shirt where the monkey stuffed his nuts. And no more Val Doonican singing 'Paddy McGinty's Goat' either," Abba said enthusiastically. Paddy glared at him, not sure how to take his last remark. Abba muttered an apology and left at speed.

'Arry hesitantly asked, "I didn't know Val Doonican was coming on the cruise, our Cissie likes him. I don't think she will like to see Val Doonican blown up, Scouse. Don't mention that part of the plan to her, Scouse. She is always on about them fancy cardigans he wears when he is singing. Cissie reckons his mother must knit 'em for him."

The lads trooped out to complete their afternoon's work.

I wouldn't swap this job for the world. Where outside of a university would I find such a group of intellectuals to participate in such earth-shattering debates?

After Paddy had stopped the machine to give the lads time to clear up he said to me, "Eh, Scouse, that idea of yours about the cruise ships for the old folks?"

"Yes," I reply hesitantly.

"Do you tink that will be applied for the Irish as well?"

I was reluctant to answer as he appeared so serious. He added, "You see, Scouse, I have been tinking. We don't have any mines in Ireland as far as I know. And there isn't many shipyards or steel works either. But we do have is lots of old people we could do with getting rid of. But I tink there will be a snag, Scouse. You see de Irish being mostly Catholic like to have the last rites said to them before they die. Now if we was to dump them in de sea as they kind of died a bit on de ship who could do dat? De Captain is not de same as a priest you see, 'cos he might be a Proddie. That would never do for our lot. I don't tink de Pope would allow it somehow."

I had an inspiration.

"That's easy solved, Paddy, my old mate. I bet you have lots of old priests in Ireland don't you? I've heard hundreds of them went to the USA as priests but came back to the Old Country to die."

Paddy replied, "Yes, I suppose we do. I seen a telly picture in me lodgings about one called *Father Ted*, there was an old priest in that."

I remarked, "I saw that myself, Paddy. Father Jack was his name – a great lad for his booze as I recall. Anyway that's what I was about to suggest. Stick a load of the old priests on the ship. There is loads of Catholics in America sympathetic to Ireland – remember all the money they used to send to the IRA? They don't have to send that any more since Tony and Gerry became pals. I'm sure the Yanks would either build them ships for you or give you some of their old cruise boats to use if you agreed to take some of their old people to make numbers up like. There are lots of them in Florida sitting around in the sun taking up deckchair space. If you had trouble getting the funding off the Irish government the Catholic Church has pots of cash anyway. They could sell some of them statues and paintings off. Eh! They would go down well on the *Antiques Road Show* or *Bargain Hunt*. Paddy, I even read they had sold an entire old church to Japan, they had it took to pieces and shipped over then reassembled it in Tokyo. The Japanese are making a fortune doing fancy weddings over there. So there you are Paddy, with all that money they could even have them ships built in Italy by good Catholics in shipyards by where the Pope lives. He could keep an eye on the job and stop the Mafia ripping you off."

"Hmm, good tinking, Scouse, you're a sharp one you are. Tink of everytink, don't ya?"

I beamed with pride and continued with my idea.

"Then when all the old priests are loaded on the ships they could spend their days chanting the last rites on a sort of rota basis. They could broadcast around the ship on the tannoy system day and night. As the old ones drop dead no matter where they are on the ship, they would be covered by the last rites and needn't worry about getting into heaven. Then it's just a matter of tipping them overboard. They would have to be wrapped in the Irish Flag of course."

I had a sudden thought and added it to my ideas to make the operation even better. I was really getting into this with enthusiasm. Ideas kept coming to me one after another. I knew how these top executives like Richard Branson felt now. I continued enthusiastically:

"I suppose to make it even more efficient they could do them in a job lot. Say ten o'clock every morning after breakfast when they have collected all the bodies they could shoot them overboard with the ashes from the stokehole. Two jobs for one, this would save time and money. I had actually thought of using the dead bodies instead of coal but I think the firemen might object, especially if it was someone they knew. Pity that. It would have been a kind of cremation, though, just the same. What about that, then?"

Paddy replied thoughtfully, "Sounds all right to me but take my old Uncle Sean. Now he is as deaf as a post, dat could be a problem does you tink? What if he missed the last rites chantin' because of his deafness and finished up in Hell with the Proddies. Me Auntie Agnes wouldn't like that. No not at all. You will have to retink dat one, Scouse."

Thoughtfully I replied, "Hmmm? Can he lip-read, your Uncle Sean, Paddy? 'Cos I think I can solve that one as well."

Before I could elucidate further on my idea Paddy said, "Oh, oh, de lads have finished, I will have to start the machine up again. We should talk about dis later on, eh, Scouse?"

The day the job came to an end and our gang of lads moved on to another site leaving me alone with the big Irishman. Paddy's boss McCriethy arrived in his pride and joy, a fully restored E-type Jaguar in which he was to meet Pontius. The plan was to move Paddy's machine up to the next lock the next day to carry out a similar operation. Paddy and McCriethy were in a huddle which erupted into a blazing row.

I was unable to hear what they were arguing about when Pontius arrived. McCriethy and him had a chat then left in Pontius's estate car to size up the next job. Paddy shambled over.

I had to ask.

"All right, Paddy? I noticed you arguing with your boss."

"He ain't my boss no more, Scouse, before the bleeder could sack me I told him to shove his job up his arse. You know he only wanted me to show his mate how to use the machine, so I told him to piss off."

"So that's what you were rowing about, eh?"

"No, Scouse, it was about my wages, he's paid me to the end of the day and wants me to work for it. He has ordered me to clean down the machine and wash his car while he is away with your boss. How long do you reckon they will be, Scouse?"

I replied, "Knowing Pontius he will make a day of it. They will be somewhere in a pub on expenses for lunch. No, I reckon it will be some time this afternoon before they're back."

I asked, "Are you going to clean his car, then?"

He answered with a kind of relish, "Oh yes, I'll clean his car all right, dat will be my pleasure."

Surprised by his reply, I declared, "Well, Paddy, it's been nice meeting you. You have done a brilliant job on those turbine pipes; the machinery is working a treat now. I have to go up to the next bridge today to do a bit of servicing. The river opens for shipping again tomorrow so I have to get things ready. I then have to visit one of my old mates in his cottage. I pick his pension up and a bit of shopping. I'm not looking forward to that. The place is a bit of a tip since his old woman died. He keeps trying to get me to have a drink of tea and something to eat but, 'Yuk!'"

Paddy smiled and offered me some advice, "Ah, you're a good lad, sure yool be all right, Scouse. If he offers you a brew of tea, do what I used to on dose occasions and drink from the udder side of de cup."

I shuddered, thanked him and added, "You should see the place. I don't think he has washed the cups since his old woman died about a year ago. She had the place as clean as a new pin, but now? Never mind, duty calls. George is a good old boy but should be in a home where he is looked after – he's in his nineties now."

Paddy laughed and said, "Sounds like a prime case for de old ones' cruise ship, eh Scouse?"

I laughed with him and stuck out my hand.

"If I don't see you later, Paddy, good luck in America. Just leave the keys to the lock hut in the usual place if you go before I come back."

We shook hands and that was the last I saw of Paddy Lopez – but not of his handiwork.

The visit to Old George was the usual nightmare. I was not looking forward to sitting through many of the same stories he told me on every occasion. The visit was different this time, for he fooled me with the tea. He must have been waiting for my arrival at the appointed time and had the kettle boiling. Before I had the opportunity to refuse he stuck a cracked filthy mug in front of me. The cup rested between the debris on the litter-strewn table that showed signs of mouse droppings amongst the crusts and discarded food.

I protested feebly, "I've just had a brew, George. Aren't you having one yourself?"

"No. No," He hastily explained. "I've only got the one cup you see? Broke all the other buggers when I was chasin' a rat. Drink up, lad, while it's still hot. I'll have one myself after you've gone."

I looked at the mug in horror – how could I refuse the old boy's hospitality without upsetting him? I kept having visions of George's tobacco-stained lips on the mug. I raised the mug to my lips and taking Paddy's advice, I used my left hand and drank from the opposite side of the rim. When I had drained the mug I placed it back on the table, smacked my lips and said, "Nice brew, George, I enjoyed that."

He looked at me and said, "Funny thing, Scouse, I didn't know you was left-handed, the same as me."

I slipped him the usual small bottle of rum and an ounce of tobacco. I made an excuse and left in a hurry, determined to get Social Services to sort him out.

I returned to the lock about three o'clock in the afternoon. Paddy's van had gone but his boss's E-type was still where he left it. That is to say the remains of his car were still where he left it. Paddy had indeed washed the car, using the fearsome machine. Written on the bonnet in penetrated letters were the words "WOOPS wrong pressure". The rest of the car looked as if it had been through a meat grinder. Paddy had wreaked his revenge on his boss.

In the lock hut I found a note addressed to me and in it he explained:

> "Scouse, I have had a great time with you and your mates. Do me one last favour. I am leaving McCriethy's van at Manchester Airport in the long stay car park. I would appreciate it if you found this note in a day or two. By the way I think it's only fair to reveal Oi am not de tick Oirishman you all tort. I have a degree in engineering and lectured at Dublin University before I took this job for a change and to acquire field experience. The position I am filling in the USA is as technical director of the company that designs and constructs the machines. If we ever meet again we must finish exploring your ideas of disposing of the old folks. I think it has great potential. Uncle Sean and Aunt Agnes are getting more cantankerous every day.
>
> "I shall be in touch when I settle down in the new job.
>
> "Paddy."

Well, bugger me! What a character was Paddy! He had kept up the pretence for at least a week and I never once suspected his true identity.

There were two results of Paddy's visit. His boss McCriethy broke down in tears when he saw his beloved Jaguar.

And on a more serious note, the pension fund secretary contacted me and asked me to present some of my retirement ideas at the next full committee meeting in London. When I enquired what he meant he said he had heard on the grapevine I was discussing my ideas with the members before notifying the committee. I wonder who snitched on me?

The gang of lads were working in my area and used the lock hut for their meals. I looked forward to great company and absolutely amazing debates and I wasn't disappointed. Today the main topic was bee-keeping. Big Al was with the gang driving the crane. He had just been left a well-stocked vegetable plot in his wife's uncle's will and was very pleased with his inheritance. There was only one drawback. On the land were a couple of bee-hives and Al didn't want them – he not only didn't want them, he was terrified of the bees.

'Arry's ears pricked up when he heard this.

"Tell you what, Al. I'll take em off your hands for a few bob, OK?"

Al replied, "I don't know 'Arry, the old uncle had them there to pollinate the flowers and fruit trees. I reckon the neighbouring gardeners might do their nut if I get rid of em."

'Arry laughed scornfully, "Bugger them, Al. They are your bees, if the greedy sods want them there, then make 'em pay. Tell you what, I'll take em off you, and if they want the use of them, I'll rent em back to them."

"I don't know, 'Arry. That means they would still be on the land."

Al was always one to make a few bob if the opportunity arose, so he thought for a minute then asked, "How much were you thinking of offering me – they're worth quite a bit, I believe?"

"Pay you! Pay you? Are you mad?" 'Arry blanched. "I was

expecting you to pay me to take 'em off your hands."

Big Al snorted with disdain. The idea of 'Arry having to pay hard cash in a deal literally made him ill. Big Al responded, "Forget it 'Arry."

The lads laughed and settled down for a good session. I saw the negotiations coming to an abrupt end and wanted it to continue – I loved these confrontations.

"What do you know about bees then, anyway, 'Arry? They take a lot of looking after, you know," I inquired innocently.

"Bees! What's so hard about looking after bees? Bloomin' heck, I've had every kind of animal and bird you can think of."

Al added, "And you ate most of them, you hungry bugger. I don't forget that swan you cooked in the oven on the dredger."

'Arry smacked his lips. "Tasty that. The daft bird was asking for it. No one pecks me and gets away with it."

Appalled, I enquired, "You didn't kill a swan, did you, 'Arry?"

Paul said, "Bloody hell, they belong to the Queen, you know, 'Arry. If she finds out you'll be in big trouble."

'Arry retorted, "Whose gonna tell her. You? I suppose you will ring up her palace and say, 'Hello my name's Paul, I work on the cut, puddling shit. My mate 'Arry has ate one of your swans.' Do me a favour? Do you think she cares about a bloody swan up here? What does she want them for anyway?"

Paul shrugs his shoulders, "I suppose she feeds 'em to her visitors. They are always coming over to England I've seen 'em on the telly."

'Arry added, "They only come here for a good feed. Them foreigners eat all kinds of weird things. I bet a good fat English swan goes down a treat at one of her parties."

The bee debate was dying on its feet, there was too much deviation, but thankfully the Fiddler chipped in, "Hey, 'Arry, it's in the local paper, they are doing a free beekeepers' course at that big house this weekend. The fruit growers are trying to encourage more apiaries in the district"

"What the bleedin' hell have monkeys to do with bees, you daft sod?" 'Arry growled at him. A few of the lads that knew what an apiary was sniggered. Tombo, an acknowledged crossword expert, enlightened us regarding the meaning of the word 'apiary'.

Puddling Paul thoughtfully gave us the benefit of his knowledge.

"Hey! Lads. Does any one of you remember a police programme on the telly called *Dixon of Dock Green*?" A few of us acknowledged we did indeed remember the programme and wondered where Paul was leading.

Instead of enlightening us he tried to persuade the others with poor memories that they should recall the blast from the past. They argued back and forth for a while; it was leading nowhere and was only diverting a good debate to the exact year colour TVs were launched. Thankfully they gave up when I enquired, "Well, Paul, what about Dixon?"

He replied, "Oh yes! Well the fella that played him? I can't remember his name though. I think it had something to do with those shops that sell tellies and other electric stuff."

Jumbo Jack, who was working with the lads that day, snapped his fingers and said, "Curry's! His name must have been Curry – they have loads of electric shops! I've never heard of anyone on telly called Curry though."

Paul had a maddening habit of doing this, giving us half a story, usually mixed up anyway, and we spent hours trying to figure out what he was on about.

I informed them hesitantly, as I usually kept out of the debate, "There was a fella called Findley Curry, I don't think it was him that acted in a cop story, I think he played Casanova."

Paul said admiringly, "Casanova, eh? He was a randy sod, wasn't he?" I was beginning to enlighten him about Casanova when I was interrupted.

"Jack Warner! His name was Jack Warner and he's dead." Billy interceded and began giving us his rendition of the theme tune. *"Dah dee, dah, dee, dah, dee, dah. Evening all."*

Most of the lads that were old enough to remember the series joined in. The others looked on wondering if they had gone mad.

"Bloody hell, Paul, what you going on about? We are trying to sort these bees out, here. I want to get on with the gardening and I can't, with them bloody things buzzing about," Big Al angrily brought the medley to an abrupt close.

Paul informed him lamely. "Well, me Ma told me he had bees and used to let them sting him for his rheumatism."

"Bugger off, Paul, you barmy sod," Big Al curtailed any further contributions from Paul. The poor fella shrank sulkily into the corner and took no further part in the big bee debate.

Brickface popped his head into the hut.

"What's all the shouting and singing about then?"

'Arry replied loftily, "We are discussing bees and apes here. Big Al's just been made the owner of millions of them. Know anything about, 'em, Brickie?"

Brickie gave him a strange look.

"I know something about bees but not much about apes," he replied with a somewhat bemused look on his face.

'Arry snorted scornfully at his lack of knowledge.

Brickie ignored him and continued, "Did you lot know if one of the little buggers stings you on the lips you're as good as dead? My granddad died when he got stung. I wouldn't go near them sods."

Big Al went visibly white at this disclosure. Tombo threw another scary fact into the pot.

"Eh! Remember that wagon driver who used to work here, Hissing Syd?"

"Yes," I replied.

Tombo continued, "Well he got a job as a porter in the hospital when he left. Do you know how he got his nickname?"

I had to admit I didn't.

"Well I was second man on his low loader with him. We were doing a long trip and had to stop in the country for Syd to have a pee, and he only stuck his pecker into a wasps' nest. I've never seen him move so fast – he leapt into the cab with swarm of the sods chasing him. Jesus, you should have seen the way it swelled up." Tombo's voice dropped to a whisper. "I had to drive the truck to the hospital and I haven't got a licence you know, I could have got caught by the cops. Eh! We had a bloody big crane on the wagon at the time."

"Get on with it, Tombo, for Christ's sake," Fiddler urged.

Slightly miffed, Tombo continued with the pecker piece.

"His tackle was in a terrible state. All that down to wasp stings, Al, don't forget them buggers are smaller than bees. Imagine the same thing happening to you?"

"What's that to do with his name, then?" Fiddler asked.

"One of the nurses reckoned his pecker was the size of a python, so they called him 'Hissing Syd'. Get it?"

"I bet his missus was made up, eh?" 'Arry remarked. The lads laughed.

Tombo stopped the laughter and ribald comments when he disclosed, "Syd wasn't married see, he had never, er, had a bit either. The nurses thought his enormous pecker was down to the wasp stings but it wasn't. He was hung like a donkey and he had never used it 'cept for peeing. He told me the nurses kept rubbing it with cream and ointment trying to get it smaller. Every nurse in the hospital came and bed-bathed him about ten times a day. Syd said he had never been so clean. He loved it, that's why he jacked in his job on the cut and got a job in the hospital!"

The lads roared with laughter, and Fiddler called him a lying sod. Tombo responded with, "It's true, on my life, every word."

Brickie rebuked, "I can't take the things you pervos discuss; why don't you lot talk about football or normal things?"

"You mean like farting festivals," Tombo threw back at him.

"I'm going," Brickie said disgustedly and left the debating chamber.

Al visibly paled when he learned these facts.

'Arry sensed triumph as he observed Al's reaction to this deadly threat to his manhood and quickly made another offer.

"Tell you what, Al, I'll do you a favour and take them off your hands for nowt, as long as I can leave 'em on your veggie plot."

"What the bloody hell do you think I am, 'Arry? I want to get rid of the sods, you daft bugger. What good's that to me?"

'Arry gave him a crafty look. "Ah! But, Al, I'll look after them. You won't have any responsibility and won't have to go near 'em. This is the best part – you and your mates get the benefit. Er, for a price, you understand?" he added quickly.

Al thought for a moment and I could see he was wavering.

"Tell you what, 'Arry, I'm going on that course this weekend, could be if I'm taught about them I might keep 'em. If it don't work out, we'll have another talk about them, OK?"

"You'll have to have all the gear, you know? It says in the paper everyone that attends has to have all their own safety equipment and they have to be there at nine o'clock on Saturday morning," the Fiddler advised.

"That's no problem, it's all in the uncle's garden shed," Big Al revealed.

'Arry asked, "Could I come with you, Al? Just in case you change your mind. You know about letting me have the bees? I may as well learn about them. I fancy being an ape man now."

Hesitantly Al agreed but tried a few obstacles to deter 'Arry.

"You'll have to supply everything yourself, 'Arry. I've only got one of those net head things and one smoke gun. The rest of the gear is only gloves and a boiler suit."

"No problem," 'Arry replied confidently. "I'll fix myself up. Pick us up Saturday morning, eh, Al?"

The meal break and debating session was over and we had to return to work. As they were about to leave Paul said totally out of context, "Then there was Z Cars, who remembers them, eh! They had a great tune, it went Dah, dee, dah, dah. Dah, dee, dah, dah."

There was a chorus of "bugger off, Paul!" as they went back to work.

I thought the next Monday should be interesting, and it was. At baggin time they trooped into the lock hut. 'Arry sat at one side, and Big Al sat as far away from him as possible. I sensed a bit of hostility between them. Fiddler faced me, making gestures and mouthing things. It appears I was chosen to be the one to ask the reason for their attitude.

"Well, how did the course go, Al? Did you enjoy it, learn much off the experts?"

He replied sullenly, "Don't mention that bloody course. I have never been so embarrassed in my life."

I probed further, trying to tease it out of him to no avail. He sat there tight-lipped.

'Arry exploded with laughter.

"You're a silly sod, Al. Gang of bloody puffs that lot, who gives a toss for them?"

Al answered angrily, "I do 'Arry, I wanted to learn things. Fat chance of that now, eh, thanks to you, you daft sod."

This was too much for the lads – we had to know what happened.

Fiddler pleaded, "Come on, Al, tell what 'Arry did to upset you so much."

Big Al glared at 'Arry. "OK, I'll best tell you the true version before he gives you a load of codswallop."

'Arry sat with a stupid grin on his unshaven face.

"I picked 'Arry up at half past eight and he had this big parcel with him. I asked what it was and the silly sod just tapped his nose, you know, the way he does?"

We all nodded knowingly, including 'Arry.

"Anyway, when we got there we met up with the others and the fella in charge introduced us to each other. Bloody hell, there was lords, ladies and all kinds of posh buggers there. There was more Range Rovers in the drive than I've ever seen together before."

"Seems like every one wants to know about bee-keeping, eh, Al?" I remarked trying to keep the topic interesting and divert his wrath away from 'Arry. Al nodded enthusiastically.

"We had this lecture and slide show on bees, very interesting it was. I never knew honey was so good for you. He gave us all kinds of facts. They reckon you could live on just honey, it's supposed to be a pure full food, you see?"

'Arry snorted with disdain. Al ignored him and carried on enthusiastically with more facts.

"For instance, did you lads know the Roman soldiers used to put it on their wounds to help healing?"

We confirmed it was indeed news to us, something we always wanted to know. Al, undeterred by the sarcasm, continued extolling the virtues of honey.

"Don't forget the monks make mead with honey."

"I believe you can get well pissed on a glass of that stuff," said

Paul, ignoring his previous bollocking from Big Al.

He got another withering glare for his trouble, then Al went on with his description of the disastrous bee-keepers' course.

"When he finished and we had a brew and some nice sarnies, he asked us if we all had brought our equipment with us. When we told him yes, he advised us to put on our protective gear as we were going amongst the hives. Another fella that works there, the apiarist, was going to demonstrate how to handle the bees and recover the honey. That's when things went wrong, thanks to that soft sod."

'Arry chipped in, "I didn't take you for a snob, Al. You should have seen the way he kissed their arses, lads."

Al, ignoring his jibe continued.

"I went to the car, got my gear, and put it on in the stables with the rest of them. There was no sign of him..." he nodded towards 'Arry. "...so we went down the orchard to the hives. It was really going well when that lunatic turned up."

Al went quiet. I could see he was raging.

"Why, what did he do?" I asked in a sympathetic manner.

"It's not so much what he did at that moment, it's the way the lunatic was dressed."

I tutted and urged him on. Al appealed to all the lads.

"Do you know what he had on his stupid head?"

"No!" we replied in unison.

"He had a bloody great shade off a standard lamp, with a net curtain draped over it. Would you believe that? All the rest of us had really posh gear on but he has to turn up like, like..."

'Arry grinned his toothless smile then let out a bellow of laughter. This appeared to infuriate poor Al even more. He jumped up and left the hut. 'Arry carried on with his version of what happened next.

"I don't know what Al's on about. Everyone except Al liked my headgear. The ape man said he had been looking after bees for fifty years and he had never seen anything like it."

"What happened next, then, 'Arry?" I asked with an eye on the clock. Pontius Pilot the foreman was due down that morning as it was pay-day – he was bringing the wages.

'Arry carried on with the tale. I could tell he didn't understand why Al was so upset.

"It was all right until I knocked the hive over. We had looked at lots of bees with our gear on. He told us to take off our gear, as the bees we were going to see next were very friendly, experimental bees.

"'Don't worry!' the silly sod said when I looked a bit nervous. 'These bees have never been known to sting anyone.' All the rest of them believed him and left their gear in the stables. Not me though, I don't trust them posh sods. If someone had nicked my er, protective hat, our Cissie would have gone mad. It was her favourite, you see?

"The ape man took us to the far side of the estate. There was just one hive there. He warned us to move slowly and speak quietly just like when you 'whisper' a horse, it soothes the bees, you see? Of course I knew all about that kind of thing," 'Arry boasted. "Didn't I have horses for years? Anyway he put his hand in amongst them, and little buggers walked all over it no problem. It was then my head protector things caught on a nail or something sticking out of the hive. I gave it a bit of a tug and the hive tipped over. The bloody bees he said were harmless went berserk. I was lucky I still had my gear with me, I wasn't trusting them sods, so I stuck it back on quick as a flash. The other silly sods had left their gear behind – ha, ha! You should have seen 'em run. I've never seen Big Al move so fast. Bloody good mate he turned out to be. He headed for the car park like an Olympic runner, jumped in the motor and pegged it. He even left the uncle's gear in the stables. Get this. Did you know the miserable sod wouldn't stop to give me a lift home? Neither would any of the other mean buggers give me a lift. Al's car screeched away scattering the gravel everywhere, and he left me to walk bloody miles. I was knackered when I got home hours later. And I had to hump that stupid lampshade of Cissie's home to make it worse."

The sound of the foreman's van approaching curtailed any further debate on the subject of bee-keeping, as the lads trooped out of the hut and pretended to look busy.

Chapter Six
Ghosts and spooky things

I DON'T USUALLY contribute much to the big debates, prefer-ring to listen and note. On one occasion I became the story teller. It was Hallowe'en and all the lads were meeting up at their favourite pub for a darts match. Unfortunately, thick fog dropped in and the challenging team from another canal had to cry off. Being the night of the spirits the conversation got around to ghost stories.

Before I accepted the employment on the waterways I was a seaman and spent time on the Mersey tugs. I also did two years' National Service in the Army.

It was a peculiar night during the miners' strike in 1984. The lads and I were in a back room of the pub, the electricity had gone off yet again. It reminded me of my time at school during the war. The teacher would have us kids sitting in a semi-circle around her on the floor as she told us stories. Then there was the time in the air raid shelters when the grown-ups told stories, while we kids were supposed to be asleep. With eyes pressed closed we would listen to many a bloodthirsty account of the antics of Spring Heel Jack, the Mad Monk, Jack the Ripper and the acid bath murderer. My favourite was the man with the electric eyes.

Tonight it was my turn. We all charged our glasses, settled down in the candlelit room and I began to relate the story of the Death of an Engineer.

"There had always been something weird about the old tug.

She was the oldest tug still working on the river – nearly sixty years old when I was in her. You know lads, she had survived two world wars and been near sunk a few times. Strange thing though, other fellas that sailed in her had kept mum about the goings on aboard her.

"Anyway, I joined her as mate with a new crew. Over the next few months all kinds of weird things happened but I never told my mates."

"What kind of weird things, Scouse?" Paul asked.

"I was getting to that, Paul. A couple of times I had been first aboard for an early morning job and saw cigarette smoke drifting in the crew's quarters. I could smell it as well. Really spooky it was. Another scary thing happened one night, when we were running light to tie up. I was down aft in the crew's quarters having a wash in an enamel bucket. The area aft of the cabin, the counter of the tug, was a ballast chamber with no reason to go in except if we were trimming the boat. We only did that in dock anyway. It was screened from the cabin by a wooden bulkhead with an access door that was usually bolted. Anyway, I had my head down swilling my face when I heard that door slam shut. I wiped my face and looked up, in time to see a figure wearing a brown boiler suit disappearing up the ladder leading to the deck. I shivered, 'cos a blast of icy air came from nowhere. All of a sudden it came to me – I realised none of the crew wore brown boiler suits. I dropped my towel and raced up on deck. There was no sign of anyone. I checked the crew – they were all in the usual places and none wore a brown boiler suit. I never mentioned it to the rest of lads."

'Arry asked, "Why didn't you tell your mates?"

I answered, "Because 'Arry, I didn't want them taking the piss out of me. You know what fellas are like."

'Arry nodded understandingly.

I carried on, "A few more weeks went by and really strange things continued. One early morning we tied up on a shipyard wall waiting for a tanker to arrive on the tide. I was on the bridge on my own at the time. As I drew alongside the quay wall it was level with the open bridge. The sailor was about to jump ashore when a figure appeared from the winding shed. It was someone I had never seen before. He stood there, a wizened old fella lit up by a gaslight. He waved the sailor back aboard and offered to hang our rope on.

Then he kind of squinted at the tug's name. When he read the name he stepped back. "Jeez!" He gasped, "Is that old cow still afloat?"

It took me back for a minute and I said, "Ah! She's not too bad."

"Not bad, you say? Phew, I was second engineer in her forty years ago. I had to jack in after Old Malam got himself croaked. The old bugger drove us mad with his haunting."

This tied in with things that had happened to me aboard her. The sailor came up to the bridge as the old man told the story.

It seems the Chief was at the engines on his own in the engine room. The Second, the man we were talking to, had gone up to the galley for a brew. He was drinking his tea when he heard the skipper double ringing the telegraph, this was followed by the wrong way alarm bell. He raced down to the engine room, brought the engine to a stop and then he saw where the Chief had gone – he was mangled up in the engine pit."

The lads gasped.

Paul said sympathetically, "Poor bugger."

'Arry added, "It must have made a right mess, all crushed up. I bet there was blood everywhere, eh?"

I continued, "Yes, according to the old fella it sure was. It gets worse though. They had to use the engine to get to a berth where they could ring for help as there was no radio aboard."

Brickie says, "Wow, that's a real horror story, Scouse."

"I've not finished telling you it all yet. At the inquest the Coroner ruled the Chief had been oiling around. He had suffered a heart attack and fallen into the engines. The old fella told us he stuck it for a few more weeks but had to give up, and he left the tugs and got a job in the shipyard. He reckoned the old bugger blamed him for his death and wouldn't give him any peace."

'Arry observed, "Now, you've raised a good point there, Scouse. Say for instance I got killed at say ten o'clock in the morning, would I get the day's pay or would they book me off the minute I was dead?"

"You wouldn't get anything, you daft sod," Brickie exclaimed. "'Cos you'd be dead."

Paul said, "Trust you, 'Arry, worrying about money even when you snuffed it."

'Arry looked peevish.

"You lot know what I mean. Would my missus get the day's pay? I bet these mean buggers wouldn't pay. Pontius would book me off right away, no trouble."

Tombo offered a solution. "Tell you what, 'Arry, if it does happen to you we'll not let on until pay day and she'll get the week's pay. Nobody would notice you'd gone anyway."

Paul added, "Except the farmers, gamekeepers, gardeners and all the poor animals you slaughter every day."

The lads laughed as 'Arry made a lunge at him.

Brickie asked, "Is there an end to this story or what, Scouse? These daft buggers are always interrupting a good yarn."

I replied, "Oh yes. Before we could get any more info from the old geezer the tanker arrived and we had to leave. The sailor said as we got under weigh, 'You know, I thought there was something funny aboard this one. I've had this weird feeling since we joined her but didn't like saying anything.'

"'What kind of weird feeling?' I asked. 'Well, the other day I went down to the cabin and I swear there was like a cloud of smoke in there.'

He stopped telling me other things that had happened to him as the skipper appeared at the bottom of the bridge ladder. The sailor made me promise not to say anything in case the skipper thought he was a nutcase.

The next day we tied up in the same place on the shipyard wall. The usual guy that worked there came out to hang us a rope on. I asked him where the old fellow was who was on last night. He gave me a strange look and asked, 'What old fellow? There is no one on duty here at night. No need for anyone. Who could get to here except by water and there is nowt to nick anyway.'

"I told him, 'He came out of the winding shed about two o'clock this morning.'

"He started laughing and said, 'I think you're winding me up. That place is only opened when we work the basin caisson and the Stores have the key. What did he look like, this mysterious fella, anyway?'

"I described him the best I could, with the sailor adding his twopennorth. The man went white. He said, 'Bloody hell, you have only described Old Fred. We dragged him out of the basin about five years ago – poor Fred drowned himself. The Coroner reckoned he had committed suicide while his mind was unbalanced. He always was a weird old fella, kept on about spooks and things when I worked with him. I remember he used to frighten me to death with his story about an old engineer, really horrible story. He used to tell it when I was having my sarnies. I'm sure the old bugger did it on purpose. Funny thing about him, I never ever saw him eating or drinking himself – strange that, eh?'

"Just then the ship arrived and we let go our rope and chased the ship.

"I stayed with the old tug through one of the coldest winters on record in 1963. Strange things kept happening. I was in a pub one night with the rest of the crew and a few pints of Guinness under my belt when I told them the story the old fella told me. I couldn't believe it, all the rest of them had suffered in the same way but didn't say anything in case the others thought them nuts.

"The fireman asked, 'Has anyone heard the groaning noises coming from the engine room when nobody was down there?' He reckoned he had heard it many times when he was aboard on his own raising steam. Even the skipper, a man not known to fantasise, admitted having witnessed the plumes of eerie smoke and the figure in a brown boiler suit moving along the deck one night when he was on the bridge alone.

"A year later she was finally sent to the breakers, old age and the Smoke Abatement Act having caught up with her.

"She went to her final resting place, ghost and all. Well, listen to what I am going to tell you. This part is really weird.

"Twice she broke away from her tug and was recovered just before she drifted onto some rocks. Then she began sinking and they had to beach her and pump her out.

"Finally, she had to be handed over to a light draft tug. One of the crew on the barge tug that ran her up the beach at the breaker's yard told me when I met him later.

"'Just as she took bottom after hitting hard, the funnel came crashing down – some idiot had let go the funnel stays. As the rotten funnel collapsed it missed the Chief by inches, he was coming up out of the engine room at that moment. Made a right mess of our bulwarks, I can tell you. But this is the really weird thing. As we were about to let go of her I saw a plume of smoke float out of the cabin door and drift down the engine room of our boat.'

"Funny thing, the tug he was a crewman on was not one of our company tugs. He had no prior knowledge of the demise of the engineer or the happenings we had experienced on the old tug."

Surprisingly none of the lads had said a word during the last part of my session, which was unusual. There were normally lots of interruptions and sidetracking. 'Arry was first to break the silence. He congratulated me and enquired, "That was a good 'un Scouse, but what's a demise when it's out?"

Brickie the crossword fiend interceded, showing his knowledge of the English language. "It means death, 'Arry, it's when you pop your clogs."

'Arry muttered, "Well why don't he use proper words, if he means dead, he should say so." He looked at me and said, "Now then, Scouse! No more posh words if you are telling us a story, OK?"

I nodded and agreed. "I shall bear in mind what you say for future reference, oh, ancient wise one."

He grinned, told me to piss off good naturedly and quaffed another pint of Guinness.

I added a bit more for 'Arry's information.

"You know you wanted to know about getting a full day's pay if you pop your clogs at work, 'Arry? Well, I can tell you this for a fact. When the merchant ships got torpedoed, or the ship sank for other reasons during the war, the sailors' money stopped the minute the ship went down. There were some exceptions but most shipping companies were mean buggers. I sailed with a fella that was at Dunkirk helping the soldiers to get away. His ship got sunk by a German bomber and he was a prisoner of war right until the end. His money stopped the hour his ship was sunk."

He replied angrily, "Bloody hell! Scouse, you best make sure! I don't want to be fiddled out of any money by these mean buggers. You're the union rep after all, and should know in case it happens…" he added, hurriedly pointing at his mates "…to one of this lot."

What a man is 'Arry, plotting to the last and beyond.

How does he go from a ghost story to worrying about his wages if he dies? The workings of 'Arry's mind are a wonder indeed.

While I was telling the story I didn't notice Trevor, the landlord of the pub, standing by the doorway. Trevor was not much of a mixer, he usually kept behind the bar and did not fraternise with the drinkers socially. 'Arry reckoned he was too posh to be the landlord of his alehouse, but he was willing to do a few deals. 'Arry put up with his aloofness because of this.

Trevor joined us at the table, something none of us had ever seen before. "Hey, Scouse, I've just listened to your story. Did you know I was born in New Zealand?"

I replied with a touch of derision, "I think you told me once or twice."

Trevor told everyone that frequented the pub he shouldn't be here, he should be back in New Zealand.

Not to be put off he continued, "Well, listen to this if you think yours was a spooky story.

"I was a ship's Captain before I became a pub landlord. I only came to the UK because my wife became homesick – fancy that, after all the years she spent in NZ, she became homesick!"

To justify his wife's odd behaviour he explained, "She's English you see? Our kids are grown up and are living their own lives. I worked in jobs all over the Pacific. I also did a few years in the New Zealand Navy. It is a very spooky country, you know. I think it's the Maori influence, myself.

"A few years ago I went to Papua New Guinea, on contract to the government there, as a harbour master on a new set of docks they were building.

"Located near my lodging, the natives had constructed a kind of fish farm. It was linked to the sea by a small canal. They used it to store captured live fish ready for market.

"I usually rose at dawn. At that time I used to go for an early morning jog, before the heat of the day and the humidity."

'Arry snorted his disbelief, "Go on, Trevor, you jog? Who do you think you're kidding? I've never even seen you walk outside the pub except to get in your fancy car."

Trevor looked down at his beer-swollen belly and replied regretfully, "I was fit then, 'Arry. I'll show you some photos if you like. Anyway, do you want to hear this story or not?"

I urged him to continue. "Yes, go on, Trevor, I'd like to hear the story. No more interruptions, lads. My kids live in New Zealand and I know there are some strange things about the place."

Trevor carried on with the story in his posh manner.

"My chosen route on that particular outing took me skirting the fish holding lagoons.

"In the outermost one swam a lone dolphin. As I skirted the enclosed water, the dolphin followed me, stopping when I stopped, swimming when I ran. That morning I never intended to circle this particular one, but for some unexplainable reason I don't understand, an incredible force, need, emotion, call it what you will, urged me to do so. All the time, as I ran, the captured creature followed me.

"Until this occasion, I had not given much thought to the plight of dolphins, or their much-vaunted reputation of being able to communicate with humans.

"In fact, to be honest, I had taken all the stories and myths about these creatures with a pinch of salt. Until this day I don't know why!" Trevor repeated. "Don't know why I did the next, seemingly ridiculous thing, but do it I did. I sat on the bank, dangling my legs into the water.

"The dolphin warily approached, stopped as if weighing me up for a moment, then incredibly, the animal lifted itself up out of the water, resting its head on my lap."

I sensed he had the attention of the lads now, the drinking and fidgeting stopped and they listened intently. Trevor went into a kind of poetic description – I thought the lads might ridicule him, but no.

"How could I describe the feeling of unbounded love that seemed to pass back and forwards between us? I sat as if transfixed, slowly caressing the forlorn creature's silky head skin.

"All the while soft noises emerged from the dolphin, similar to the purring of a contented cat. I am sure to this day I was being pleaded with for help to release the unfortunate creature."

'Arry made a genuine enquiry. "Do them fish bite, Trevor?"

Brickie snapped at him, "Shurrup, 'Arry, this interests me. I'll tell you after. Go on, Trev, tell us what happened next."

"This strange ritual must have continued for nearly an hour, when the associate I resided with appeared. He'd become quite concerned because I'd been missing for so long, and would certainly be late for an arranged meeting.

"The dolphin, sensing his approach, withdrew its head and swam just out of reach, where it lurked, balefully eyeing my companion.

"I went to the meeting but could not concentrate. I made my excuses, virtually racing from the building, I returned to the lagoon. When I arrived a few natives with spears surrounded the lagoon making preparations to slaughter the trapped animal.

"Fortunately, the leader spoke English. I haltingly communicated to him, that I would be prepared to purchase the dolphin from them.

"He evidently thought a madman had entered his life. He wondrously asked me, how I could possibly eat such a large animal? Meanwhile, in his native tongue, he evidently told his companions about the mad European's idiotic request.

"They slapped their thighs with glee, bellowing howls of laughter.

"All this time the leader gave me the same looks mad people must receive when they commit something outlandish. In the end he acknowledged the seriousness of my request, when I handed him a bundle of money.

"At last he relented, took the money thankfully, indicating that

I was now the proud owner of the dolphin. He also, very good-naturedly offered to kill and butcher the animal for me. Appalled at this suggestion I indicated my intention to keep the dolphin alive.

"He shook his head at the antics of this strange foreigner.

"Next came the tricky bit. Having purchased the animal, I then had to persuade the natives to free the beast. They could not cope with this further madness. Packing their spears, they went on their way, chortling amongst themselves.

"I stood contemplating my position, in an increasing dilemma.

"All my working life I had never made a decision without considering all aspects of the situation. Now I had committed this momentous act, on the spur of the moment in an alien environment, and didn't know what to do next.

"The dolphin swam towards me, lifted its head on the bank, made strange noises, splashed back into the water and headed towards the far side of the lagoon.

"I still had no idea what to do. The animal turned back to look at me. Seeing I wasn't following, the dolphin repeated the procedure of resting its head on the bank, making noises and then swimming to the far side.

"Somehow I knew I must follow the animal. I raced around the lagoon, remembering seeing some rough stop planks and wire netting fences on my morning run. Sure enough, when I arrived at the spot, there they were. They blocked a manmade canal leading to the sea.

"On the seaward side of the dam, another dolphin lingered. The captured dolphin went into a frenzy when it observed me feverishly dragging the planks and netting clear.

"Before I removed the last couple of obstacles, the animal leapt the barrier.

"It paused a moment before finally escaping into the wide sea. The dolphin returned to where I stood, bringing its companion with it. They both raised their heads out of the water, as if to thank me. Then, with a flip of their tails, they headed out to sea."

'Arry gasped, "Bloody hell, Trevor! That's hard to believe but a good story."

Paul added, "It's true, you know! I've seen it on the telly; them fish is very smart. The Americans used them in the war to put bombs on ships. That French diving fella Jack Custard was always on about them."

Trevor cut in and informed us, "I haven't finished yet. There's a lot more to tell if you want to hear."

Paul answered, "You bet I want to hear. I wish my old woman was here, she loves them dolphins. She has heard you can swim with them, she's always on about it."

I ask him, "Why don't you take her then? You don't have to go abroad. You can go dolphin watching in Cornwall or Devon. I've seen porpoises all around the coast in this country when I was on the boats."

Brickie remarked scornfully, "That's because he's too tight to pay. Go on, Trevor, what happened next?"

Paul retorted angrily. "It isn't 'cos I'm bloody mean, it's just because the silly cow can't swim a stroke, see?"

Trevor continued, "I slumped to the muddy bank exhausted but elated. At the same time I had this incredible feeling of loss, as my new-found friend headed towards freedom.

"I saw them for the last time as they performed a perfect dual somersault before disappearing out of sight.

"Years went by. I told the story on many occasions. Some of my friends believed me, others gave me that funny look. But I knew what I had witnessed, and it lived with me continuously.

"I joined Whale Watch, becoming very involved with preservation organisations, spending most of my free time when possible, attempting to refloat stranded whales and dolphins.

"Then disaster struck. One of my friends' kids died. He was a smashing young lad, he used to come everywhere with us. He was more like one of my own. I thought the world of him. He loved fishing and spent all the school holidays on his dad's boat. He loved to see the whales and dolphins, you see? The lad had a camera and photographed hundreds of them."

Trevor sniffed back a tear. Evidently the memory still affected him.

He continued, "We assembled in my friend's house having a

kind of wake for his son. His father is of Irish blood and treated funerals different to most ones I had been to in the past. It was more like a party. He reckoned that's what they did in the old country.

"We all wrote on a piece of paper where and how the body of the child should be interred. Should he join his ancestors in the family grave? If so, well, there were three sites to choose from. Should he be cremated? These alternatives were put forward.

"Discussions of this nature always took place in his family with all members and friends having the opportunity to voice their opinions. We wrote our suggestions on the papers and handed them to his father, him being head of the clan so to speak.

"Without exception we all indicated the same idea. The child should be cremated and his ashes scattered on the sea area he loved so much.

"Arrangements were made. The ceremony was carried out from the deck of his boat. The day was memorable, sad, but in a way uplifting. The choice of funeral arrangements could not have been better. Even the weather was kind to us that day, although it was the season of unexpected storms.

"Twelve months later, on the anniversary of the occasion, I found myself serving as a reservist Captain in a coastal vessel on a training cruise in the locality. I knew our course could take us past the spot were we scattered the ashes. With a small deviation it would bring me there at the exact time a year later since the ceremony.

"I told my friend, and he purchased a remembrance wreath of his son's favourite flowers prior to my sailing. All his family signed the attached card.

"We duly arrived at the spot at the appointed time, and stopping engines we wallowed in a lazy swell. I cast the flowers into the waves muttering a few words of er... well, should we say a greeting... or farewell to his departed son.

"The crew stood silently to attention, as a mark of respect to the memory of the child most of them knew well.

"Wiping a tear from my eye, I returned to the bridge, started the engines, and set sail for my home port.

"I had my back to the location where I had cast the wreath, so unfortunately I didn't witness the first part of the next half hour, but a number of the crew described it in detail to me afterwards.

"My first officer drew my attention to the occurrence first. I ignored his suggestion to look back. Then the lookout suggested, 'You should look aft.' I shrugged the idea off, being still emotionally moved by the event.

"More urgently he insisted, 'Captain, you really should look astern. I can't believe what I'm seeing.' Something in his manner, an unaccustomed display of emotion, persuaded me.

"Reluctantly I turned around. In amazement I witnessed two dolphins following the craft, pushing the wreath ahead of them.

"They trailed us almost to the port area, and before breaking away and returning to the deep, they performed a perfect dual somersault, then taking the wreath with them they disappeared out to sea.

"The descriptions of events from various crew members, tallied almost completely.

"On my turning my back on the scene, the two dolphins had appeared as if from nowhere, to carry out their strange rituals.

"Hard case sailors were brought to tears by the events that day. Now try to tell me that it's nonsense, this link between dolphins and humans. Nobody will ever convince me it does not exist.

"I like to think that the dolphins pushing that wreath are the animals I encountered in Papua New Guinea.

"It gives me great comfort to imagine the dolphins are returning my favour of freeing one of them, by welcoming the soul of that lost child into their domain."

Trevor concluded the tale and without another word he left the room.

From that day to this he has never mentioned the strange occurrence again, and never joined us at our usual table in the back room. Silence prevailed for a minute or so as the lads contemplated the story, until Brickie remarked, "Well, that was some story – sad, but I wouldn't have missed it for the world. I have read lots about dolphins saving people from shark attacks. I've never seen one in the flesh so to speak, but after what Trevor told us I am going on dolphin watch next time we go on holiday to the Canary Islands."

'Arry persisted with his question, "But do them fish bite, I want to know?"

I answered, "No, 'Arry mate, they don't bite. They will give you a nasty suck though. Why don't you lend them those teeth of yours so they can have a good feed?"

My remarks lightened the atmosphere after Trevor's sad story.

Brickie informed 'Arry, "Dolphins are not fish – for your information they are mammals."

"What's a mammal when it's out?" Paul enquired.

Brickie replied knowledgably, "Bloody hell, Paul. Your education is sadly lacking. Mammals give birth to live young ones and have to breathe air just like human beings."

Paul replied, "Daft that! How can they go under water if they do?"

Brickie brushed him off impatiently. "Ah, go and find out yourself. I'm fed up educating you."

Paul muttered, "Well, I seen a picture once. It was called a *Boy on a Dolphin*. This kid he was a film star. I can't remember his name."

"Get on with it, Paul, for Jesus' sake," 'Arry rebuked him.

Paul continued, "I was telling you, hold your horses. This kid sat on the dolphin's back and they swam underwater for hours. I just wondered, that's all."

Tombo said with a laugh, "You spend too much time trying to grope that usherette of yours instead of watching the picture, Puddling my old mate."

His remarks brought forth roars of laughter and Paul shrank into his corner.

Trevor's wife Sheila popped her head in and informed us, "It's nearly time, lads, the fog is still thick as a bag. Are you having a lock-in?"

After a hurried discussion we decided to stay for a while until the fog cleared. A few minutes later the bell rang and we heard Trevor calling "Time, gentlemen, please."

After all the other customers had left the blinds were drawn and the doors were firmly locked. We ordered another round. After we settled down 'Arry asked, "Any more stories to tell us?"

Brickie remarked, "Eh, 'Arry, you only live across the cut. Aren't you going home? Cissie will be pissed off with you if she misses a lock-in."

'Arry exclaimed, "Are you mad? You heard what Sheila said. You can't see a hand in front of you out there."

Brickie retorted, "You never can see when you leave here, 'Arry. What's the difference tonight?"

'Arry gave him a withering glare and replied, "Sod you, Brickie, it's all right for you. Your missus is away, otherwise you would have been gone hours ago after drinking the one pint she allows you."

I sensed a row brewing and hurriedly interceded, "Well, there is another story told to me by a shipmate years ago – do you want to hear it?"

The lads agreed and I began, "You'll like this one, 'Arry, it's about a fella with the same name as you. It's all about the Divil that lives in Liverpool..."

Paul, who cannot handle his beer as well as the rest of the lads, informed us in a slurred voice, "Ooh the Devil. He's a rum bugger isn't he? You know the Irish fitter, Mick? I got on his goat one day. He told me that all us non-Catholics will go to Hell when we snuff it, and the Devil will make our lives a misery for ever."

Tombo retorted, "Are you thick or what? How can the Devil make your life miserable if you're already dead, you barmy bugger?"

'Arry interceded, "Ah, leave him alone, Tombo. He's half sloshed and he can't hold his pop like us. Paul go and have a kip over in the corner – I'll finish that pint off for you. Come on, Scouse, are you going to tell us the story, then?"

"OK, 'Arry here we go. A couple of my shipmates, Harry the Hump and Freddy the Foot were on their way back to their ship after a piss-up in the south end of Liverpool. They had missed the last bus and taxis were out of the question because they were skint. On the way back to the docks they had to pass a very spooky graveyard well known in local folklore for its weird happenings. Now to go around the graveyard meant a detour of nearly half a mile. There was a short cut through, but no one in their right mind used it at night. The two pals arrived at the gates. Harry the Hump decided to go for the short cut much against the advice of his mate, who reminded him it was the worst night of the year to contemplate going through.

"'Why's that?' Harry asked.

"'Cos it's Hallowe'en, soft lad,' Freddie told him.

"'Sod all them daft stories, I don't believe in all that crap. See you on the other side, you yella rat,' Harry laughed as he disappeared through the gate.

"Freddy set off dragging his clubfoot for the long trek around the cemetery, muttering a dire warning to his pal.

"'You'll be sorry. Don't say I didn't warn yeah.'

"After a few hundred yards into the cemetery Harry began regretting his decision. Marble statues of angels and cherubs appeared to come alive as clouds passed over the moon. He dismissed them with a scornful but nervous laugh as he reassured himself of the stupidity of bogeymen. As he arrived at the centre of the cemetery by the chapel he thought he heard pipe music coming from a huge family crypt. He hesitated, peered into the semi-darkness, then leapt behind a gravestone as he observed dwarf-like people dancing around a huge figure sitting cross-legged on a marble tomb. The full moon illuminated the scene. Holding his breath Harry sneaked closer. The central figure had horns on its head; hoofed feet on the end of its legs. The thing played some weird pipes. The small figures carried tridents. As they danced about they aggressively thrust them at each other. They emitted horrible screams of pain when the weapons struck home. The huge figure turned his head towards Harry and gave him a withering glare.

"Its eyeballs sparked with fire, and smoke appeared to come from its mouth. Harry was terrified as he tried to conceal himself. He shook with fear. The pipe sounds ceased, the noise of the chattering demons hushed. Harry could not help himself; he had to peep around to see what was happening. The moon bathed the empty scene in a weird white light. Relief engulfed Harry – it was all a trick of the imagination, he assured himself. About to continue his journey, he felt a tap on his shoulder. Slowly Harry turned around, absolute terror making his movements jerky. He confronted the most horrendous animal, person, thing, he had ever encountered even in his wildest nightmares.

"It said, 'What's your game, pal? Do you know who I am? What are you doing in my cemetery on this special night? Do you know what tonight is?'

"Four rapid-fire questions thrown at Harry in quick succession by the bellowing monster. The demons danced and urged the demonic figure to inflict all kinds of excruciating things on the shaking Harry.

"'Hang him up, whip his bum, feed him Senacot, squash his tum.'

"'Shurrup you little sods,' the thing shouted. 'Go and frighten some old women and leave me in peace will ye. I'm sick of you lot.' The demons scattered but not too far away.

"'Now you, arsey bags, down to business. Right I'll start again. Question one. Do you know who I am? You've got to the count of three to get it right or I'll zap you were it hurts with this.' He pointed his fork at a concrete angel. There was a burst of flame and the severed head of the monument crashed to the ground.

"'Ha, ha,' the monster laughed. 'They'll blame them rotten kids for that in the morning. Serves them right – little sods they are, always peeing behind the gravestones.'

"The Divil began to count. 'Now, one, two…'

"Panic-stricken Harry shouted, 'You're the Divil, Mister. Me gran told me all about you. She always said I'd go to the Divil if I never behaved myself when I was a kid, and here I am.' Harry whimpered, 'Sorry I never believed you, Nan.' His gran was buried nearby, and Harry hoped by appealing to her it would help his situation.

"'Ha. Sensible woman your gran sounds. Right, you got question one right. Question two. Now what special day is this?'

"Before Harry could offer an answer the Devil reached out, touched him on his humped back and whistled admiringly.

'Phew, love your 'ump. Wouldn't mind that meself. Eh, tell you what. Seeing that today is my birthday and I was going to ask you for a prezzie, or roast you alive if you never give me one, would you mind if I took your 'ump? I rather fancy meself with one of those.'

"Harry was astounded. 'Yes. Yes, go ahead, mister. Er, I mean, I know I'll miss it, but for your birthday, well, you're welcome if you really want me er, 'ump.'

"The Devil pointed his taloned finger at Harry, who shrank back in fear, then he recited a little poem.

"'*Umpty, umpty, on his back.*

"'*Come over here and don't go back.*'

"The hump disappeared off Harry's back and for the first time in his life he was able to straighten up. Harry was beside himself with joy.

"'OK pal,' the Devil told him. 'Go on, get out of here, and remember, if you ever come again at night, bring me another prezzie, OK?'

"Harry continued his short cut at speed. He burst from the gates and almost knocked his mate Freddie the Foot over.

"'Jeeze, Harry, you look great, where's your 'ump?' Freddie inquired. Out of breath, Harry gasped. 'You're not going to believe this, Fred, but I met the Devil in the cemetery and he took me 'ump off me back. It's his birthday you see? And he demands a prezzie from anyone who passes through at night. Lucky for me he chose me 'ump for some reason.'

"Freddie asked, 'Eh, Harry – do you think he would do something about me club foot if I went through? I mean he can have it for a prezzie if he wants. I'm fed up with the damn thing.'

"'Give it a go, matey,' Harry advised. 'Look what he did for me. It's our lucky night, I reckon.'

"Freddie nervously entered the cemetery. He had nearly reached the chapel when the Divil confronted him. Freddie dropped to his knees babbling with fear. The Divil spoke. 'Where's your 'ump, you miserable scrote?' he bellowed.

"'I haven't got one, Mr Devil. I've never ever had one.' The Devil breathed out fire. 'Don't roast me, mister. I only came here to see if you could do something nice for me,' Freddie pleaded.

"The Devil roared with laughter.

"'Get up, you whinging brat. Don't you know it's yer lucky day? It's me birthday, and I'm feeling great. I've just scared the crap out of another fella who dared to come through here without a prezzie for me so I stole his 'ump. Now for the good news, because it's me birthday I'm going to give you a prezzie. This here 'ump doesn't really go well with my image and it don't fit right anyway. So my friend, through the goodness of my heart I present you with this ere 'ump.'

"With that the Devil recited the Umpty poem.

"'*Umpty Umpty stuck to me,*

"'*Detach yourself and onward flee*

"'*To that fella over there*

"'*Without an 'ump he looks so bare.'*

"There is a flash of bright light, the hump flies through the air and attaches itself to Freddie's shoulder,

"'Oh no!' the Devil screams. 'Daylight come and I've got to go home.'

"With that last remark the Devil disappeared and Freddie was left with an 'ump and a clubfoot."

Roars of laughter greeted the ending of the tale.

Sheila came into the room.

"Shush lads, keep it down. You'll have the cops down on us."

When she had left 'Arry said, "What a load of old cobblers that story was. But I love it. I must tell our Cissie that one when I get home."

The fog cleared about two o'clock in the morning and we made our way home. Paul, still the worse for wear, staggered along with me. As he lived on my route I escorted him to his front door. His mother was waiting. She gave me a severe telling off for getting him in such a state and keeping him out so late. Just before she dragged him indoors, his last words were, "Eh, Scouse, does the Divil really live in that cemetery at Liverpool?"

I had a day or two with the piling gang to see the introduction of a new bonus scheme. The lads were working on a big job at the far reaches of the navigation, way out in the country. Located nearby were the ruins of an old Abbey. 'Arry and his mate Puddling Paul were acting as the supply boat ferrying materials from a wharf where a lorry could deliver the load to his narrowboat. Come knocking off time 'Arry, usually first on board the tug, hung back when it arrived. The tug transported the lads to a pickup point where they caught the works bus.

"Nice night," 'Arry explained furtively. "I'll think I'll have a walk down the towpath tonight. You lads get off, I'll make my own way home."

As soon as the lads were out of earshot the speculation began. I loved these debates and welcomed the opportunity to be involved and contribute to the nonsense

'Arry's motives were suspicious as he only walked if there was a profit to be had.

Brickie reckoned, "'Arry has a deal on with the local farmer and is waiting to get us out of the way. The tight bugger doesn't want to let us in on it."

Dave said, "I don't think so. He didn't even try to do a deal with those pleasure boats that tied up by us. He never misses a chance to skin those daft buggers and flog them his tatty canal memorabilia. He's been acting funny since he came to work this morning. I think he's ailing – or he's love-sick! It's not like 'Arry to be so quiet."

Sam remarked, "Love sick – 'Arry! You must be joking? The only things that bugger loves is his ale and his wallet."

Puddling believed he had the solution. "His in-laws are stopping with them. I saw their boat passing up the cut at the weekend. 'Arry hates the sight of them, he calls them his 'out-laws'. There is only the one bed in the cottage, you see, and they all have to share."

"You what?" Brickie exclaimed. "How many of them are you talking about? Surely they sleep on the boat?"

Puddling explained, "No, they all live in 'Arry's cottage when they turn up. When any of his relatives visit, they all come ashore. I reckon they get fed up living on them shitty boats and crapping in a bucket. There is only 'Arry, and an old uncle who has a cottage in Yorkshire, that live ashore out of his family."

I added my contribution to the great 'Arry debate. "I've heard about his uncle, he's the oldest fella left in a company house. He was born there, and except for his time in the Army has lived there all his life. He must be near a hundred."

Puddling informed us, "He is the only one with the knowledge you know? He learned to read in the Army in the big war. But I was telling you, that's 'Arry's family. This lot of visitors are some of Cissie's mob."

Puddling counts them out on his fingers: "Well, in the bed will be 'Arry and Cissie, then there is Cissie's big fat sister Nelly, she always turns up for her birthday present. Boy, I mean fat! Have any of you lot seen her?"

"Only saw her once," Dave remarked with a exaggerated shudder. "She was in that alehouse by the lock 'Arry boozes in. Puddling is right she can't half put it away. She can out-drink 'Arry' any day. Bugger me! You should have seen her doing a clog dance for some tourists. The landlord had to stop her just as she was about to climb on a table. The council announced a minor earthquake on the local radio and urged people to go outdoors in case their houses collapsed."

Roars of laughter greeted his description of Nelly's entertainment. Brickie, who didn't appear to share our humour, called Dave a "barmy bugger."

Big Al offered an explanation. "Maybe that's why 'Arry doesn't like her, eh? If she comes for her birthday 'Arry might have to pay for her booze. Cissie can shift her whack as well. I saw her at that 'do' we had when George retired, she supped the place dry. No wonder he's keeping clear. He doesn't want to fork out, the tight bugger."

Sam, who had been quiet until now, asked, "Eh, I have often wondered – how do they go on having a jump in those little cabins? They always seemed to have lots of kids, but they all slept in the one little place. And if Nelly is as big as you lot reckon, how would it be possible?"

I laughed and retorted, "Trust you, Sam! You always want to know the gory details, why don't you ask 'Arry? I'm sure he will share his intimate secrets with you. Maybe you could write a book about it called, um, 'How to Screw the Crew in a Little Space'?"

Sam blushed with embarrassment, and because he was the focus of attention he retreated out of the cabin.

Puddling continued, "I reckon Nelly is all of eighteen stone or even more. 'Arry told me her old man has to trim the boat with pig iron ballast when she gets aboard or they will capsize. It must be a bugger having to do that every time she moves, eh?"

Brickie looked at him scornfully and remarked derisively, "You believe anything 'Arry tells you, Paul. I don't know!"

Paul ignored his comments and continued listing 'Arry's visitors. "Then there is Tom, her husband. He's not a bad fella except when he's pissed – then he will fight any bugger. He's a bit of a tea leaf as well, he's been in and out of nick most of his life. Him and 'Arry nearly killed each other last year when Tom swiped some of 'Arry's pigeons. 'Arry reckons he ate them."

Paul dropped his voice to a whisper and looked around furtively when he informed us: "I know he didn't eat em 'cos he did a deal with that Welsh fella in the Pet shop, the one 'Arry deals with. One of the pigeons was a racer belonging to Trevor the landlord of the Big House. 'Arry had coaxed the bird into his loft a couple of days before.

"You all know about what he does. It's a sweet little racket he has going."

Dave enquired, "If they always come back to 'Arry's loft, why didn't the pigeons fly back to his place then that time?"

Puddling revealed, "Cos that bugger in the pet shop is smarter than 'Arry and knew they would fly back to 'Arry's so he wrung their necks and sold em to the Chinese takeaway. There was Pigeon Chow Mien on the menu that night, lads, although Fong Loo still called it chicken."

Big Al informed us in a knowledgeable way, "It's not the only pets he sells em. I've heard when he can't shift some of the pets and things they go to the Chinese or that Indian place as well. I'm sure the last time I ate something from the Star of India it didn't taste right. I don't go there any more not since I had the Alsatian Vindaloo."

Puddling carried on from where he was before the interruptions. "I tell you what 'Arry is like! You know that fella in that picture I saw when I was a kid?"

I considered his latest remark. Should I ask who he was referring to? I weakened. I had to enquire who. "What fella in what picture, Paul?"

He informed me in a knowledgeable way, "That fella that spoke to the animals – Doctor Somebody. Who! That's it. It was Doctor Who!"

Paul seemed to spend his life in confusion about names and characters. I informed him patiently, "It was Doctor Doolittle. Doctor Who was... Oh! Never mind, Paul. It was only a story anyway, it's not true, you know?"

Paul protested, "You might not believe it, Scouse, but I have seen 'Arry with horses – he's what is known as a 'whisperer'. He can make a mad horse as quiet as a kitten."

Two of the other lads confirmed 'Arry's skill with animals. They had personally witnessed him in action with a mule that had a splinter from a fence stuck up its arse, Tombo revealed.

"You know what horses and that are like, always rubbing their backsides on posts. Well, this one wasn't so lucky – he got stabbed by a splinter. The vet couldn't get near the mad bugger. 'Arry just kind of said something in a low voice and the mule settled down, turned its arse to 'Arry and he whipped the bloody great lump of wood out."

Dave added, "It was stuck right up the poor animal's bum. I wouldn't have gone near it – talk about a mad mule!"

Paul continued telling us about the landlord's pigeon.

"'Arry had already put out feelers to claim a reward if he could catch the pigeon. Ha, ha! And while he was doing that he already had the bugger in a box."

Paul, after deviating to side issues, returned to the original theme, "Oh, and yes! I was telling you about 'Arry's in-laws. There's that bloody horrible kid of theirs, Snotty, I think his name is, at least that's what 'Arry calls him. That's the one 'Arry really hates, he's a little swine."

I enquire, "Why does he hate him so much? He's only a little kid. I saw him once when they were tied up by 'Arry's in their boat last year. He looked all right to me. I gave him a tanner."

Puddling explained with a shudder, "Because he stuffed one of 'Arry's ducks."

Sam asked, "Surely he was only trying to help Cissie? 'Arry's a bad-tempered bugger sometimes."

"Didn't he tell you? I thought everyone knew! The bloody duck was still alive. Snotty tried to shove an orange up the poor duck's arse," Puddling replied.

Big Al enquired, "Why did he do that?"

Paul enlightened him. "Because some posh chef on the telly mentioned duck *à la orange*."

"Ah! Bugger off, you daft sod!" Brickie refuted the story and asked, "How do they fit in the one bed, anyway? Imagine 'Arry with two women in one bed! The mind boggles."

Sam added, "What's more, how do you fit an orange up a duck's arse?"

Big laughs all around as the lads speculated on 'Arry's ability to entertain two women at once and the dimension of a duck's anal orifice.

Dave, returning to the original query, asked, "Well, come on then, explain – how do they fit in one bed?"

Puddling replied, "Oh, I don't know. I do know 'Arry only has the one bed 'cos Pontius gave it to him when him and Cissie came off the boats and moved into the cottage. When you look at the size of 'Arry and Nelly it makes you wonder, doesn't it?"

Big Al observed, "Those cottages have three bedrooms – maybe he has beds in the other rooms?"

Puddling squashed this idea. "Well, I can tell you he hasn't, because all the furniture for upstairs has to go through the windows and I helped move him in. Besides one of the other bedrooms is his pigeon loft and the other one has the ducks and hens in."

Silence prevailed as the lads contemplated the inside of 'Arry's cottage.

Al exclaimed, "Bloody hell, it must be Noah's ark in there! Who in their right mind would want to sleep in 'Arry's house?"

Paul declared, "His relatives do. Mind you, they are all barmy buggers, if you ask me?"

"I bet they're using the clothes-line method," suggested Brickie.

Puddling asked, "What's that? 'Arry's not a Catholic, you know!"

Brickie retorted, "What the bloody hell has religion got to do with it?"

Puddling replied, "I thought it's something to do with birth control. You know, like the rhythm method the Pope uses. We talked about it the other week."

Roars of laughter from the rest of the lads greeted his statement. Brickie snorted.

"You're a daft bugger. Spare me from idiots! The Pope doesn't use it himself. He doesn't have sex, you daft sod, he's a celibate. I explained last week it is what he tells the Catholics to do when they are having a jump. Don't you ever listen?"

Puddling replied peevishly, "Huh! He hasn't got much to celebrate if he doesn't have his end away."

Brickie exclaimed, "Oh, I give up. Let's get back to the rope they used, I read about it in a history book. The rope method is what they used in the doss houses in Liverpool when they were full up. They stretched a line across the room and the lads hung over it until a bed was available."

His explanation brought forth snorts of disbelief from the lads. Brickie got annoyed when his explanation was scorned, and he rebuked the lads bad-temperedly.

"Don't you know nothing, you lot? You should try reading something more than comics and the sports page of the paper. Bugger you lot, I'll not tell you anything again."

Brickie slumped in the corner of the cabin sulking. Sam tried coaxing him out of his sulk.

"Ah, come on, Brickie, don't be like that. It's just we can't imagine fat Nelly and 'Arry hanging over a washing line. Bloody hell! You'd need a ten-inch tow rope to hold their weight."

Big Al laughed.

I asked, "So what do you think 'Arry is up to? It's not like him to walk home – it's a good way to his place."

Brickie rejoined the debate. "I reckon he is staying on the boat. He would do anything to get away from his in-laws. Yes, that's it. I bet he is going to kip on the boat until they bugger off."

Sam said, "Well, good luck to him. The White Lady walks the towpath at night. I wouldn't sleep up there for a big clock. That place is scary."

"Don't be so bloody stupid," Brickie laughed. "No such thing as ghosts, my old lad."

Paul objected to Brickie's opinion.

"It's true. Me old uncle was fishing there years ago and he saw her. She was a beautiful nun in the Abbey and got murdered by the boss monk fella 'cos she declined his advances."

His description brought forth roars of laughter.

"Bugger off, Paul, you've been reading too many of your old lady's romance books. For your information Abbeys didn't have nuns, they had monks."

Paul retorted, "For *your* information I can't read and this Abbey *did* have nuns anyway. My old uncle swore he saw her, did you ever see his hair? Snow Bloody White he was. He reckoned it happened when he saw the ghost."

Sam informed him, "Eh, Paul! I hate to tell you this, but your old uncle was a piss artist. He most probably had the DTs."

Paul asked with a cunning look on his face, "All right then, smart arse? How does the Pope tell the Catholics how to do the business if he never has a go himself? Answer that one if you can!"

Brickie answered with despair, "Oh God! I thought we had finished with that one. Tell you what, why don't you ask your mother when you get home? She must have used some kind of weird method to produce something as thick as you."

Paul undaunted replied, "Ah, sod you, Brickie. If you won't explain it properly I'll ask Beryl, she's a Catholic."

I asked, surprised, "Bloody hell, Paul me old pal, are you still knocking around with her? I heard she had given you the boot. Is she still an usherette at the flea pit?"

He retorted, "She gave me the boot, my arse! I finished with her when I caught her on the back row of the pictures with the bloody horny chimney sweep. I didn't fancy her after Black Bob had been giving her one."

"How come you are back with her then?" I enquired.

He replied philosophically, "Well it's like this, Scouse. I had to make a choice. Either I had to pay to get into the pics or put up with dirty black hand marks all over her. I mean – the price of getting in the pictures these days..."

Further debate was curtailed as the tug reached the wharf and the lads clambered ashore to join the works bus for the journey home. I left them to travel in the bus and used my own car.

Next morning I was the first to arrive; the tug remained berthed with no sign of the crew or passengers. I had evidently got there before the works bus. It was a lovely morning, so I decided to sit on the tug and await the lads. To my surprise I found the cabin door unlocked, but not broken open. Oh! It looked like we'd had a visit from kids. I wondered what they had nicked this time.

The kids are a menace, especially when their school holidays are combined with long daylight hours. I knew the tug skipper, Jim, thought he was safe in this berth in a remote spot. I was about to enter the cabin when I heard a loud snore coming from inside. Cautiously I climbed down the ladder to find 'Arry fast asleep, spread out on the deck with one of the lad's coats wrapped around him and a life jacket under his head. So it was true! 'Arry did sleep in his cap and Wellingtons. I noted this fact for future debates. Trying not to disturb him I lit the gas ring and put the kettle on. As I placed the water bucket on a stool it over-balanced and crashed to the deck, sloshing water all over the sleeping 'Arry. He sat bolt upright with a howl of fury.

"What the bloody hell did you do that for, Scouse? You daft sod, you could have given me a heart attack!"

I apologised. "Sorry 'Arry, I didn't mean it, the bucket fell over. What are you doing here anyway?"

"Oh, Scouse, don't ask!"

After telling me not to ask he immediately began to reveal his night to remember.

"What a night I've had. Hey! Do us a favour? Look at my hair, will you? Has it gone white?"

'Arry removed his cap to reveal an almost completely bald head with one or two tufts of straggly hair. The sight of 'Arry's gleaming white pate threw me for a moment. In all the years I had known him I had never seen him capless.

"Er, no! 'Arry, you seem quite normal. Why should your hair be white?"

As I had never seen his head before how could I say anything different had occurred?

He replied, "Oooh! Paul's uncle was as white as snow when he saw her."

"Seen who, 'Arry?" I enquired. This was developing into an 'on the cut' classic. I hoped the lads didn't arrive before I got the full story out of 'Arry.

"It was her all right, as white as a ghost she was. Really scary, and she called my name."

"'Arry!' she said, 'Come back, 'Arry, It's me, 'Arry.'

"How would a bloody ghost know my name, Scouse? I nearly shit myself, I can tell you. Do you think she wants me to join her, Scouse? Like, as a ghost I mean?"

He suddenly reached over and felt my arm. I stepped back and asked with alarm, "Hey 'Arry, what's your game?"

He assured me, "It's all right, Scouse, I'm just making sure you're real."

I coaxed him to reveal all.

"You had better tell me what happened, 'Arry. The lads will be here shortly."

Looking at my watch I remarked, "In fact they should have been here now. I wonder what's happened to them this morning? Do you want the lads to know you spent the night on board here?"

He replied in alarm, "No way, Scouse! That's the last thing I want. Them buggers would really take the piss out of me. Eh! Do us a favour? Tell em you picked me up on your way here this morning."

I hesitated. "Ah! I don't know, 'Arry? I don't want to get mixed up with one of your daft plots."

He persuaded me to agree by making an offer I couldn't refuse.

"Go on, Scouse! I'll give you that narrowboat hooter you fancy."

I immediately consented to give him a cover story. I have always fancied the hooter since I first saw it in the collection he usually sells to the tourists.

"Well, come on, 'Arry, spill the beans if you want me to cover for you."

"All right then, I'll tell you. I made up my mind to do a bit of fishing and it got a bit late so I decided to kip on my boat last night. I felt a bit tired and couldn't be bothered going home, you see?"

I knew he was lying but didn't make a comment. He scanned my face to see my reaction. I kept a brilliant poker face and nodded approvingly as if it made sense to me.

"It was about midnight and I settled down for a kip. I left the door open 'cos it was so hot. I must have fell asleep when I heard this moaning noise and something kind of scratching on the outside of the cabin."

'Arry paused and listened.

"Are you sure those buggers haven't turned up yet?"

"Whoa, 'Arry! Never mind them, what happened next? I bet you was scared, eh?"

He obviously lied again. "Not really, I just thought it was the wind and a tree rubbing on the boat. Anyway I looked through the door and there was no one there. I went ashore to have a pee and that's when I saw her. She came from behind a tree. Bloody hell, Scouse, I was frozen to the spot. I had heard of the White Lady but never really believed it. You know Paul's uncle reckoned he saw her years ago but we put that down to his booze."

"What did you do, 'Arry? I would have buggered off it had been me, I can tell you."

"Well, I did, but the bugger started chasing me down the towpath shouting my name. I heard this insane cackling as well, like mad laughter. Then there was a crash and a horrible howl. I didn't look back until I made it here to the tug. I know where they hide the key, so I got into the cabin and locked myself in."

"The door was open when I arrived," I pointed out.

"Oh, yes, I opened it up at daylight. Ghosts don't do any haunting in the daylight, Scouse. It's a wellknown fact. Anyway I had to open the door, it was stifling in here. I couldn't hardly breathe."

"What did the White Lady look like?" I asked.

"Real scary, I don't mind telling you. She was about seven foot tall, all white of course and hovering about a foot off the ground. She had a really ugly face. I thought other people that had seen her said she was good-looking. Me, I thought she was an ugly cow. Mind you, I didn't take much notice of her – I was running most of the time."

Without a pause he asked, "Eh, Scouse, have you got anything to eat? I'm bloody starving!"

For someone that had taken no notice of the White Lady he had described her in detail. I offered him a share of my carry-out which he wolfed down.

"What are you going to do for the rest of the day, 'Arry? A couple of butties won't keep you going all day."

He replied in between mouthfuls of my last sandwich, "Puddling's got the makings of a brew on my boat. I'll go to the pub by the bridge at dinner time. Don't worry, I'll sort it out."

The sound of an engine curtailed our conversation.

"Here! Sounds like the lads have arrived now. Say nothing, Scouse. Don't forget what we agreed?"

"Aye! And don't you forget the hooter you promised me," I reminded him.

The skipper Jim was first aboard and greeted me as I emerged from the cabin.

"What the hell are you doing here, Scouse? How did you get into the cabin?"

I climbed out of the scuttle followed by 'Arry. The skipper exclaimed, "Bloody hell, here he is, lads. We've been waiting for you, 'Arry. That's why we're late."

'Arry explained without a qualm, "I didn't ask you to wait around for me, did I? Scouse picked me up this morning. We've been here ages. I had to open the cabin up to make a brew – it'll be baggin soon. We wondered where you'd been until now. I thought you had slept in. Come on, let's get to the job before

Pontius turns up and starts giving us earache."

As the lads clambered aboard the tug 'Arry asked the skipper, "Where's Puddling?"

The skipper explained, "His old woman told us he is having a day off – he's hurt his leg or something. We'll cover for him as long as Pontius doesn't turn up and ask for him, OK?"

As we travelled to the site the probing began.

Brickie asked, "So you walked home, 'Arry? It's quite a distance to your place – you must have been pretty late getting home."

'Arry was non-committal.

Brickie continued, "Did you miss out on your supper? It was your favourite night, wasn't it? Baby's head pudding?"

Again there was no response from 'Arry.

Brickie tried another angle "Puddling tells me your rellies are visiting. That'll be nice, eh?"

There was much nudging and winks as the lads observed 'Arry's reaction to Brickie's query.

Oh! Oh! They were up to something, I detected the signs. 'Arry, a master of deception, suspected a trap. I observed his brain working before he answered casually with a classic attack rather than an explanation.

"You know what is the trouble with you fellas? You don't get enough exercise, that's why you're knackered. Look at you lot! You ride to and from work in the bus. The tug takes you to and from the job. You have cars at home and don't walk anywhere. Eh! They even have them drive-through burger places for you lazy sods. Take me for instance. I don't have a car and I walk everywhere. That's why I'm fit as a fiddle. No, Brickie, me old mate, a little walk of ten miles or more after a day's hard work means nothing to me, pal."

His statement astounded Brickie.

"You're joking! Fit as a fiddle, 'Arry? I've known you for years and never seen you walk anywhere except to clear your snares and rob stuff out of the fields. You're a cheeky bugger, 'Arry."

Big Al made a remark that gave me a clue to 'Arry's encounter with the White Lady.

"Eh! Brickie. Never mind walking, 'Arrys quite a runner when he has a mind, eh lads?"

His revelation was greeted with much sniggering. The tug arrived at the site. As the lads dispersed to their various tasks 'Arry whispered to me, "Scouse, these buggers are up to something! Find out what you can for me, will you?"

Al was driving the crane. I knew from past experience that he was the worst at keeping a secret, so I went to have a brew with him at baggin and tried a few questions.

"What was that about 'Arry running, Al? I've never seen him running – can't imagine him getting up speed."

Al blushed and began waffling not very convincingly about the day he got chased by the bees.

"Come on, Al, what have you buggers been up to?"

I try to persuade him to spill the beans. After much interrogation at last he confessed.

"It was 'Arry's brother-in-law Tom's idea. We went to tell Cissie 'Arry was walking home. Puddling the daft bugger, told him he thought 'Arry was staying on the boat all night. Anyway Paul and Tom went into a huddle and we left Paul at 'Arry's cottage. That's when they cooked up the daft idea."

"So you did see Paul this morning, eh?"

Al replied, "Oh, yes. Part of what Jim told you was true. Paul has got a sore leg and can hardly walk. We ran him to the hospital for an X-ray before we came here this morning. That's the real reason we are late."

I tried a further question.

"OK! That part is clear now, what happened last night?"

Big Al revealed all with a sigh.

"OK, Scouse, you win. We met up in the Big House pub for the weekly darts game. One thing led to another and in the end we decided to teach 'Arry a lesson for cutting us out of that deal with the spuds."

"What deal with the spuds?" I enquired. "Oh, never mind, get on with the story."

Al continued, "We'd all had a few pints except Brickie – you know him, he only has the one. Talk got around to the White Lady and where 'Arry was tied up in his boat. You know the landlord of the Big House is pissed off with 'Arry over his pigeon?"

"I heard," I reply.

"Well, he supplied the gear from the amateur dramatic mob that meets in the pub. They did a play about the White Lady and all the nun's clobber was still in the back room. The stilts were Paul's idea to make him look taller. We had a great laugh putting his make-up on. The landlady sewed an extension onto the nun's habit to cover the stilts. Anyway after the darts match the landlord shut the place and we all piled in the 'get you home pissed' bus.

"Brickie drove us to them woods by the site. Paul hid behind a tree with a torch ready to shine on his face, waiting for 'Arry to appear. Me and Dave sneaked over to the boat and scratched on the roof and made groaning noises. When we heard 'Arry on the move we pegged it and hid in the woods. I wish you could have seen what happened next, Scouse. 'Arry came ashore for a pee. He was in full flow when Paul burst out of the woods. What a sight! 'Arry stood there with his dick hanging out and pee-ed down his leg right into his wellies. We were in hysterics. Then 'Arry started to run down the towpath. Jeeze, I didn't know he could move so fast! Paul called his name to tell him it was a joke but he kept going like a greyhound. Paul chased after him on his stilts. That's when it happened. Paul tripped and fell into a culvert and 'Arry disappeared into the night. We had to carry Paul all the way back to the bus. What a bloody good night, though! That'll teach 'Arry to cut his mates out of a deal, eh?"

After I finished laughing I asked, "So when are you going to tell 'Arry it was a joke, then?"

Al was shocked by my suggestion. "Me! You must be joking? I'm not telling him – do you think I'm mad? None of us are telling him it was a set-up!"

I was puzzled by his logic and asked, "But if you don't tell him you scared the shit out of him, how does that pay him back for cutting you out of the spud deal?"

"Bollocks to the spud deal," he replied. "I don't want 'Arry doing one of those vendetta things on me, I saw what he did to that Farmer Grabber. I've got to get the crane going. See you later, Scouse."

'Arry, as usual, came best out of the White Lady incident as he related a much-exaggerated version of the event in his local ale-houses. The landlord of the Big House had to bite his lip when 'Arry held forth in his bar. Wisely he didn't want the vengeance of 'Arry brought down on him either.

Chapter Seven
Wartime comrades

I DECIDED TO spend the day with Big Al – Alfonso Oliver. Height about five foot one, thin as a rake.

Al, alias 'The Rabbit', alias 'Il Duce', alias 'Hands up Monty's coming', had a number of other nicknames allocated by different workmates and he answered to all of them. He was good company and had a fund of stories about his time on the waterways and his service in the Italian army.

'Arry and the rest of the gang had gone to the pub for lunch, leaving Al and me on our own.

We were sitting in the sun when Al opened his tucker box and began eating his meal. He noticed I wasn't eating and asked, "Where's your mungano, Scouse?"

I had promised 'Arry I wouldn't reveal that he had spent the night on the tug. As I had given him my lunch, I lied, "Ah, I forgot my sarnies today, I was in a hurry this morning."

Without hesitation Al shared his food with me. I was working my way through an enormous salami sandwich reeking of garlic when I asked, "Hey, Al, how come you are in England, anyway? I mean we have crap winters here, wouldn't you sooner be in sunny Italy?"

He replied, "It wasn't always sunny where I lived, Scouse. We lived in the mountains, lots of snow there in the winter and we were very poor family. My mum had fifteen kids and she was married three times. I don't know half of my family. Anyway I like it in England. I could have gone back to Italy after the war but

I was already involved with my missus. We have a nice cottage with a big garden and I've got that vegetable patch now, as well; what else could a fella want, eh?"

I like collecting stories. Al's sounded good so I asked, "You were a prisoner of war then, Al?"

He replied, "Yes, I got taken prisoner in the desert. We were doing all right until Monty came along with his bloody Desert Rats. Lots of us Italians worked on the canals and farms when they shipped us to Britain. It was better than having your arse shot off in the Army, I can tell you. Anyway, the Italians gave up after a while, so in a way I wasn't a prisoner of war any more, was I? Did you know we had German prisoners working with us on the canals in the war, and just after as well? The best jobs were on the farms – you got lots of good mungano on the farms. Then there were plenty of those lovely Land Girls!

"That's where I met my missus, she was in the Land Army. She was picking spuds the first time I saw her. Hey, Scouse! I bet you didn't know they had women working the boats on the canals as well."

I admitted, "No I didn't, Al, that's news to me. You seem to have had a good time in the war."

He laughed, "It wasn't too bad on the canals, either, we got lots of goodies off the boat lads. That's when I first came across 'Arry, he was a wheeler and dealer even then.

"Lots of the Germans stayed here after the war as well as the Italians, and lots of other people who became stateless when the Ruskies took over their countries."

I informed him, "I'm learning a lot of things today, Al."

He revealed more. "Eh, Scouse, you know one of them yourself, Helmut. I don't know his second name. He is in our union branch, I've seen him at meetings."

I shrugged my shoulders, unsure who he was referring to.

Al continued, "You know him? He lives on them first set of locks, he has all them kids. They are all grown up though, now, his eldest lad works on the dredger. I heard he is taking over his dad's job and cottage on the locks when he retires."

Al explained who he was – much to my amazement. I knew he

had a slight accent but I didn't know he was German. I made up my mind to find out more about Helmut.

I was intrigued by Al's story and invited him to tell me more. "So tell me how you were taken prisoner?"

He continued with his story.

"Funny that. I was a dispatch rider and got lost in a sandstorm. It was on the coast road, I was tail-end Charlie in a convoy. We were retreating, the whole British Army was chasing us. Just my luck the bloody motor bike broke down – sand in the carb, most probably. Anyway, there I am in the middle of nowhere, water running out and the sand thick as a bag.

"All I could do was huddle down by the bike and cover my head with my coat. Eventually the wind died down and the sand cleared. Not more than twenty feet away from me was an Italian army lorry.

"Two fellas were working on the engine, head down and arse up. Thank goodness. I started heading towards the truck, thinking they are from my mob, when I heard them speaking in English. I didn't know what to do. Being a dispatch rider I had a pistol, we had nowhere to carry a rifle, you see? For the first time since I got in the Army I pulled it out of my holster. I sneaked up behind them and said…"

He stopped in mid sentence and I urged him to continue. He replied, "Oh, I am ashamed to tell you any more – you will tell the lads and they will take the piss. It's bad enough the nicknames they already call me."

I urged him to finish the tale. "Go on, Al, I promise it's between you and me – I won't tell a soul."

After considering my promise he replied, "OK, if you will keep it for yourself then I will tell. I speak English well now after all these years, but I'll have to go back to the training camp in Italy so you will understand properly. We had the fascist pig that came every day to lecture us. He told us we would soon be ruling the world especially all of Europe but most of all Britain. He said we would only be taking back what belonged to us anyway as they were all part of the Roman Empire. The Roman army had only gone home years ago to sort a few problems out. The people in those countries knew we would be coming back some day and would be glad to see us. He was a right bull-shitter, Scouse, but many of the lads believed in that crap. Anyway, he said we should be prepared for the time when we invaded Britain. He brought an interpreter with him. Another head case, he had been a cook on a liner, and when it called in Britain he jumped ship. He became a butcher in the Liverpool market before the war. His job at the training camp was to teach us phrases we had to use when we landed in Britain. Can you imagine hundreds of Italians repeating parrot fashion what he taught us?"

I replied, "Sounds funny to me, Al!"

He continued, "Funny – you could say that, but it could have got my stupid head blown off. That is what I was ashamed to tell you. There was only a couple phrases I could remember..."

Al stopped talking and a grin appeared on his face before he continued.

"This is what I said to the two guys bending over the truck. Wait for it, Scouse, you won't believe it but I swear on my children's life it's true. Picture the scene in the middle of a war, three fellas lost in the desert. There's me with a gun in my hand shaking like a leaf and I said to the enemy: 'Would you like to sample my Italian sausage, Missus?'"

For a few minutes I remained silent as I took in his famous words, then Al and I exploded into laughter. After we settled down I urged him to continue with the tale. He agreed but first looked up-river to check if the tug was returning.

"OK, the lads will be back soon. I will have to tell you quick.

"One soldier turned around and all he did was laugh in my face. I ask you? There is me, a deadly enemy soldier pointing a gun at him and all he did was split his sides with laughter. This pissed me off so I gave him another order. 'Hey Missus! Don't fondle the black puddings if you're not gonna buy them.'

"When the soldier finished laughing he said to his mate in perfect Italian. 'Look here Tom, we have a Wop Chum, with a Pop Gun.'

"His mate appeared from behind the raised engine hood and pointed a sub machine gun at me. He said in Italian, 'What do you think, Guiseppe? I have got a bigger weapon than you, and I heard you Wops were built like mules.'"

Al's story was brilliant. I was eager to know the outcome as I could see the tug on the way back bringing the lads from the pub. Stifling the urge to laugh again I asked seriously.

"What did you do then, Al?"

Al confessed, "I did the only thing I could do under the circumstances. I chucked the bloody stupid gun into the Mediterranean. Lucky for me the British lads both had Italian relatives and a sense of humour. How many of my mates got shot for asking Allied soldiers questions like that, I wonder? That idiot at the training camp couldn't speak English at all, and the fascist pig never sussed him out.

"The two Brits were interpreters, following the action and interrogating prisoners. There was nothing I could tell them. I never had a clue what was going on. I don't think even the Italian Generals knew themselves, it was chaos out there. I didn't even know where I was except the sea was alongside the road. Anyway they were decent fellows, they shared their rations and water with me. Before I got the job as dispatch rider I was a truck driver, so I knew these wagons inside out. They never had a clue about Italian vehicles because they had only captured it a few days ago. I fixed the truck, we loaded the bike in the back and we drove like hell until we caught up with your Army. I stayed with them helping to keep the trucks going, they treated me good. I was out of the stupid war so it all ended happy. Eventually I was shipped back to England and you know the rest."

I remarked, "Wow! Some story, Al."

He replied, "If you think that's a good one, get Helmut to tell you his story next time you have an hour or so to spare. You'll have to hurry though, he is due to retire soon and I believe he is going back to live in Germany. He has inherited a pub over there, lucky sod."

As the tug came alongside he said, "Don't forget, Scouse. Mum's the word."

I made it my business to contact Helmut and we became good

friends, but I didn't get the opportunity to hear his story before he retired and left for Germany. I kept in touch by letters. He did well and loved being back in his own country.

In letter after letter he urged me to come on a visit to see his pub.

I was fortunate to have a cousin that travelled to Europe, particularly Germany, quite a bit on business. He knew the district well where Helmut had his pub. I had a couple of weeks' holiday owing to me. My wife couldn't come at the time as she was booked on a WI course.

I went along with my cousin to keep him company. The pub was in a small town located on the banks of the River Rhine. Helmut and his wife Betty ran the small riverside pub-cum-restaurant. I realised as soon as I saw it that this was the type of establishment I would be happy in. Character oozed from the place. With its half-timber structure and tiny windows, it looked like a really old drinking house. (I didn't know when I first saw it that it had been rebuilt after the place was bombed to rubble by the RAF.) My cousin dropped me off and arranged to pick me up again after he finished his business in a week or so.

Across the front of the building hung a weatherbeaten board carrying the legend in Gothic German, 'Helmut's Place'.

Helmut ran the bar, served the food and entertained the customers. Helmut and Betty gave me a warm welcome and showed me proudly around their place. They didn't take in guests. I was given the only spare room.

Betty and Inge ruled the kitchen and prepared the dishes, but kept well clear of the bar.

Every night I enjoyed a variety of tasty meals and the company of Helmut and the other customers.

They introduced me to the variety of German regional foods his accomplished wife and sister-in-law prepared every day. They were fantastic, but if I had consumed the enormous portions they served as a matter of course I knew I would have had problems with my weight. After much tactful persuasion they reduced my helpings to a manageable size.

I learned that once a month Helmut took to the kitchen himself and prepared a special dish, Haggis with Whisky sauce for a Scottish night.

The regulars loved it, and on these evenings it was advisable to get a seat early. The shrill of recorded bagpipes rent the air as a kilted Helmut ceremoniously marched in with the Haggis. The evenings were completed by Helmut's renditions of some of the famous poet's masterpieces, in English with a brilliant Scottish accent, or translated to his native German when requested.

Late in the evening, when all customers had been served their food and only a few hardened drinkers remained, it was his habit to sit down with them enjoying a tot and a yarn. We lounged on an assortment of chairs and benches around the pride of the place, a huge ornately-tiled heating stove.

Helmut was multilingual and welcomed the opportunity to practise his skills with the different nationalities that frequented his establishment, mostly crews from the river craft.

He was surprised and quite pleased that an Englishman enjoyed drinking Schnapps, while most of his regulars invariably drank Scotch.

He introduced me over a few sessions to the variety of flavoured Schnapps in his collection. What a collection – some bottles and clay Schnapps pots had been in the pub since his great-grandfather opened the place. Miraculously surviving the war, they had remained intact and unopened.

Until Helmut educated me, I was not aware that there was such a selection available, but I relished the opportunity to be enlightened. We yarned the best parts of many a night away on a variety of subjects, enjoying each other's company. Sometimes I went behind the bar serving the customers when Helmut was busy. It was a nice change for me and an experience I really enjoyed.

Inevitably our reminiscences evolved to our wartime experiences. After one particular lengthy sampling when the regular clientèle had left, Helmut and I sat by the stove and had a nightcap. That's when he recounted his incredible tale of woe.

Before he began telling the tale, Helmut explained that no offence should be taken by me. A bit mystified at this request I assured him that everything he told us would be taken in good heart.

Indicating a series of four portraits adorning the walls, he explained. Picture number one was his great-grandfather, the person responsible for the construction of the original establishment way back in the seventeenth century.

The other three pictures were of his grandfather, father, and finally himself.

It was the custom of the family that all the first-born sons were christened Helmut. My friend Helmut began his military career as an infantry soldier taking part in the invasion of Poland. He made no excuses or apologies for the conduct of Germany at that time. He just shrugged his shoulders when I asked his opinion and stated, "That's the way it was then. The whole nation was caught up in either a national madness or..." he paused for a moment considering his reply, "...as I see it we were a winning team after years of depression and defeat in the First World War. Eh! And you all know what it's like to be on the winning side! I mean, take your football leagues for example. Anyway, those times are past, thank goodness."

I never pressed him on his political allegiance before and during the war. I remember thinking, what would I have done under similar circumstances?

He had gone through the action in Poland without pain or wounds. On returning to Germany he had been sent for retraining as an artilleryman at his request.

"I got fed up walking across Europe watching the artillerymen ride in trucks, it seemed a good idea to me," he explained. As a member of a trainee gun team he had been ordered to a park with an ancient artillery piece to fire a birthday salute to Hitler. There occurred a premature explosion in the gun, wounding Helmut in the leg and taking the sight of his left eye. After a period in hospital he was evaluated as unfit for service and invalided out of the Army. As far as he was concerned his military career was at an end.

This is where in his life Helmut reckoned his run of bad luck began.

As the war progressed and more and more men were enrolled

into the armed forces, Helmut found himself surrounded by cripples, old men, women and children. There was nobody of his age
group left in Civvie Street. Helmut felt very lonely as all his mates
were recruited and posted. One day after a particularly violent
row with his father, Helmut found himself at the local Armed
forces recruiting office. He had received a letter ordering him
there to have his disabilities reviewed. He was decreed fit for limited duties by a panel of military doctors. He could have become
an Air Raid warden or some other mundane official in his home
locality, but he craved companionship amongst men of his own
age again. On the advice of the Navy representative, Helmut volunteered to serve on the Pocket Battleship *Tirpitz* in the catering
department. He did this principally to get away from the father he
didn't get on with. Surprisingly, despite his injuries, he was
accepted. The German military was scraping the bottom of the
barrel at this stage of the war. He was dispatched to the ship with
no training, after the issuing of a basic uniform, documentation,
travel warrants and instructions on where to go.

At the time the battleship was at anchor, bottled up at Kåfjord
in Norway taking no part in any actions. She did however pose a
serious threat to the Russian convoys by her presence, and was a
constant thorn in the Allies' side.

In Helmut's opinion the ship could never have sailed into
action, as she was seriously undermanned. Most of the remaining
crew consisted of semi-disabled sailors similar to him, and old
men brought out of retirement. All the young fit personnel had
been drafted to the U-boats. He also reckoned there was not
enough fuel oil in her bunkers to take her to sea, let alone fight a
battle. The idea of the Allies worrying about the *Tirpitz* attacking
their convoys, manned by partial cripples paddling the giant ship
into action like a Roman galley, tickled him considerably. He
paused in his narration to have a chuckle.

"Wouldn't British intelligence have liked to have known those
details?" he inquired, looking directly at me.

Helmut reckoned it was the best draft in the German navy and
couldn't believe his luck as he pottered around on the stranded
ship. The mooring where the ship lay was in a spectacular fiord.

He happily planned to see out the rest of war in Norway, painting and polishing the ship and learning how to cook. When off duty he supplemented his meagre wartime diet by fishing, a pastime he loved. His fresh fish contributions were very much appreciated by his messmates. He very rarely went ashore as he found the justifiable resentment of the Norwegians hard to bear.

Except for the futile attempts of the RAF to bomb the ship and the Royal Navy's human torpedo attack, he lived a satisfactory life well clear of the wartime hostilities.

One day a telegram arrived notifying him of his father's death.

Granted three days' compassionate leave he headed home to settle the family affairs. The journey in peacetime usually took less than twenty-four hours. However, because of the Allied bombing it took him four horrendous days by ferry and train to complete the ordeal. Though issued with haversack rations for the journey they soon expired in the extended period of travel. His life took a downward turn as hunger and fatigue wore him down. Without handouts of food from fellow travellers Helmut would have been in a sorry state.

His mother was long dead; he was never overly fond of his father whom he described as a severe and cruel taskmaster. Of his stepmother there was no word. He rather liked the lady and sympathised with her for having to tolerate his father's vicious temper. On the hazardous train trip he passed the time planning the improvements he would make to the business on his release from the Navy.

The train eventually stopped a few kilometres outside of his hometown due to track damage. He picked his way on foot for the remainder of the journey, through a bomb blasted landscape.

By this time he was virtually starving, sustained on the final few kilometres with visions of a warming meal awaiting him at 'Helmut's Place.'

Turning the final corner of his journey home he confronted his inheritance in all its glory. Courtesy of the damned RAF, he now possessed a wonderful ornately-tiled heating stove surrounded by a pile of rubble and a half-wrecked pub.

At this point in the story Helmut produced a picture showing the pub before the war, then newspaper cuttings containing photos of the devastating war time scene. I was amazed that his brother had rebuilt the pub so accurately.

Helmut continued telling me his story. He recalled slumping against a wrecked cart surveying his misfortune, when two Military Police demanded his papers. In a daze, he handed his leave pass and identity card over to them. Of course, he should have been back on duty the day before. The MPs immediately arrested him for being absent without leave.

They marched him to the nearest police station located in the town hall, and deposited him in the underground cells despite his protestations.

"At least I was fed before they informed me I was to be shot in the morning as a deserter," Helmut added with a grin.

The German government, concerned at the number of desertions, was implementing this policy ruthlessly at that time. As the night progressed he gave up protesting to the officials about the injustice he felt. Helmut fell into black despair.

Eventually the authorities were convinced of his innocence when the town mayor, an old family friend, spotted Helmut as he left the cells for the last time on his way to the firing squad. His friend vouched for Helmut's loyalty with the Field Court Martial officials who had passed the summary sentence. On his release he contacted the naval authorities. He was immediately ordered back to his ship in Norway. Meanwhile his father had been buried and his relatives had gone their separate ways, glad to be away from an obvious RAF target. The town mayor informed him that his stepmother, unknown to Helmut, had left his father months before, unable to abide his violent moods

This suited him, for there was nothing to keep him at home. He looked forward to being back in his ship away from the nightly bombing raids.

He had just boarded a train when the Military Police collared him again. They issued him with a fresh set of travel documents and ration cards. They informed him that British midget submarines had sunk the *Tirpitz*. Helmut was crestfallen as he realised his cushy berth was at an end. He had also lost a great deal of personal belongings he had left in the ship.

His new orders were to proceed to La Pallice, a submarine base located in France.

The idea of being in submarines terrified Helmut. For two days he sweated as he journeyed towards the horrible fate he knew awaited him in the U-boats. Nervously he re-read his instructions. For the first time he noticed an attached note. The relief he felt was unimaginable. Because of his disabilities he was not going to sea, he had to report as a cook in the shore base. Things at last were looking up for Old Helmut.

Travelling the long journey to France he thanked his good fortune, congratulating himself on his brushes with death in Poland, the exploding cannon and lastly the firing squad. Not to mention the RAF who seemed to have a personal vendetta against him. Learning to cook would be of benefit when he returned to 'Helmut's Place' after the war – things couldn't be better. At this time he realised Germany was being defeated, and Helmut was planning for the boom that would inevitably arrive at the cessation of hostilities.

He arrived at the base in France only to find it also flattened by RAF bombs, much to his chagrin. He was amazed at the resilience of the French. No doubt used to this kind of thing, they had quickly reopened cafés and restaurants before the dust had settled and the roar of the bombers receded into the distance.

In a roadside café he sat, drowning his troubles. Incredibly, an old shipmate recognised him as he strolled by. He sat down and shared Helmut's wine. The man explained he had transferred to U-boats from the *Tirpitz* to get extra money. He was sick of the tight discipline he suffered on the surface ships. "All those inspections, bugles blowing, officers coming out of your ears. I never joined up for that. No way! Action! That's what I joined up for. It's a doddle," he explained. "There's very little spit and polish and the women go mad over submariners. Officers are young fellows, pretty good on the whole except for..." he lowered his voice cupped his hand over his mouth. "...a couple of Nazi bastards in the crew, except for them I'm having a great time."

After a few more bottles he persuaded Helmut to join the

Submarine service. The German Navy, short of volunteers at that time, welcomed him with open arms and immediately drafted him to an outward-bound sub as a cook. By the time he sobered up and realised his ghastly mistake, he was at sea. Pitching about in the damp smelly sub he consoled himself with the extra money he could save to rebuild 'Helmut's Place'.

His boat was only at sea for a short while running at snorkel depth when she was attacked by a British Sunderland flying boat. The bombs blasted the sub, forcing it to the surface. As it was impossible to dive due to hatch damage, the Captain surrendered to the flying boat. He was informed by Aldis lamp that a British destroyer was on its way to accept his surrender. He assembled the crew on the outer casing and informed them of the following.

"Men," he bellowed to the dejected sailors. "There is good news and bad news. I shall give you the good news first. For you the war is over. You have fought a valiant war and nobody can condemn you for this occurrence. There is a British ship on the way to pick us up."

He looked at his watch and added. "It should arrive in about ten minutes. I suggest we sit the rest of the war out in a peaceful POW camp." A half-hearted cheer greeted his words. A bold fellow from the rear of the assembled crew shouted. "If that's the effing good news Captain. What's the effing bad?"

The Captain shuffled his feet in embarrassment before answering.

"Well, men!" he pushed forward his Chief Officer. "You all know and love the Chief Officer, a true and loyal member of the Nazi party." The crew responded with muttered curses. The bold sailor who spoke before sheltered by the assembled crew shouted. "Yes! We know the Nazi bastard, the sneaky shit."

The Nazi Chief screamed dire threats at the man. The crewman responded with a Churchill gesture over the heads of his shipmates. Despite their critical circumstances a nervous giggle swept through the ranks. The Captain continued, unable to control a smile on his face. "Well, to save the boat falling into enemy hands our bold Chief has set the scuttling charges for…" he again consulted his watch. "…about five minutes from now. It's been a long war and I am really weary. It's a beautiful summer day. I suggest we all check our life jackets and go for a swim."

With those final words the Captain leapt over the side and swam frantically away from the submarine rapidly followed by the rest of the crew. After a few minutes' swimming they witnessed the U-boat exploding and disappearing beneath the waves. The flying boat continued to circle the scene, presumably guiding the destroyer to their position.

The British ship did turn up on time and rescued all but one of the crew from the water. It appears the Chief went down with his ship, a good Nazi to the last. Whether he did so voluntarily nobody was prepared to say. The death of the Nazi Chief took the pressure off the rest of the crew, particularly the Captain, who was accused by the British of breaking the surrender agreement by scuttling the U-boat.

To a man, the crew all pointed the finger of blame for the sinking of the sub at the Nazi when they were questioned individually.

On landing, they were taken to a remote camp in Scotland. After a short while with the consent of his comrades, Helmut volunteered to work in the camp cookhouse. It was a great job, just what he wanted, an opportunity to learn the culinary arts. A friendly Scots cook took him under his wing. He even taught him the art of making haggis to celebrate Burns Night in the officers' mess – an occasion celebrated by both captors and captives. It was a happy camp except for the midges; with a beautiful summer at its height, Helmut enthusiastically absorbed the Scottish culture. Eventually, after much coaching by his Scottish friend he could recite long passages of Burns in the poet's native tongue. He also translated passages into German for the benefit of his fellow prisoners. There appeared to be an unspoken agreement in the camp between the prisoners and the guards that nobody should cause any problems. They all wanted to see the war out with the minimum of fuss, far from the hostilities. But fate had other ideas. An ardent Nazi U-boat crew were captured and imprisoned in the camp. Everything changed from then on. They encouraged confrontation, no co-operation and generally caused chaos. Those who refused to obey their orders were subject to court martial.

After a couple of idyllic months enjoying his captivity, things had again changed for the worse. Without explanation, he was with the original prisoners trucked to the docks and loaded onto a ship for passage to a POW camp in Canada. At the time he was devastated, but secretly glad to be away from the Nazis.

On the ship he consoled himself with the fact that he was still out of the war and a long way from hostilities, and saving money – with, if the opportunity arose, a good chance of escaping to America. The good old USA, a place he dreamed about. He had many relatives there and he knew they would shelter him if he could make it to New York. But he wasn't that worried, he could see the war out in Canada. Helmut felt sure he could worm his way into cookhouse duties again

Their troopship was torpedoed two days out of Scotland, sinking almost immediately. He barely had time to scramble down the listing deck and launch himself into the sea for the second time in his career. The difference was this time it was dark. Alone on a life raft that gave him sanctuary from the cold water, he realised how fortunate he was to escape intact from the doomed ship. The icing on the cake was that he had been plunged into this latest predicament by his own side.

Dawn arrived. Helmut stripped off his wet uniform and rigged a mast from a piece of driftwood. He hung his clothes on a makeshift clothesline and opened the emergency ration locker. He was eating the dry crackers and sipping the water when he heard a shout from nearby. Two sailors swam towards him through the floating rubbish. Helmut pulled them aboard.

Even though they were British crewmen off the ship, Helmut was glad of the company, any company was welcome. Fortunately Helmut was able to communicate with them. He shared the precious rations with them, they told him that if he hadn't rigged the mast with the clothes they wouldn't have spotted him.

They spent the next hour assuring him the Royal Navy would soon pick them up. Helmut believed they did this more to keep their own spirits up than to comfort him.

A roaring and gurgling erupted from the sea close to the raft.

Much to their alarm they observed a German U-boat surfacing. As the sub crept closer he recognised the friend he had met in France who had persuaded him to join U-boats. He was waving at him from the conning tower. Helmut quickly donned his clothes and life jacket and prepared to be rescued.

One of the German sailors threw him a line and he scrambled aboard the sub with difficulty, his body being buffeted by the waves. He could not stand up because his injured leg had gone into a cramp spasm. As he lay there trying to recover the sailor explained it was this U-boat that had sunk the ship Helmut had escaped from. The U-boat Captain blamed the British for carrying POWs into a war zone and he was really mad at them. They had already rescued a number of German sailors and the U-boat was now overcrowded. The Captain refused to allow the English sailors aboard. A crew member gestured for them to stay clear with a sub machine gun as they attempted to follow Helmut. For one horrible moment Helmut thought they were about to shoot the two survivors but he relaxed when a submariner tossed some stores to the sailors aboard the raft.

Helmut lay breathless on the deck thankful for his escape but sorry for the forlorn-looking sailors they were abandoning. He often wondered since that occurrence if the men were rescued. As he struggled to regain his senses he heard a loud warning klaxon shrieking.

The submariner who had been assisting him shouted, "Enemy ship coming." He raced for the conning tower. The hatch closed, diesel engines burst into life. Helmut observed a distant plume of smoke on the horizon. At full speed the sub raced from the scene of the sinking. The diesels stopped, the thrashing propellers ceased. An ominous silence followed. Propellers began to rotate again driven this time by electric power. Helmut realised with horror what was to follow. The boat began to submerge and rushing water washed him again into the sea. Luckily he still wore his lifejacket. He was into the water for a third time in his career.

Miraculously a ship approached. Closer and closer she came. Helmut could see the periscope of the U-boat close by scanning the target as he bobbed about in the wide sea. Thank heavens an alert lookout spotted his waving arms – or had the U-boat skipper warned them of his presence. Who knows? She stopped, lowered a boat and rescued him. He recognised the large flag of Chile painted on the side of the ship. Chile was a neutral country. "Great!" he thought, "South America, here I come. Lots of German immigrants live there and I should be at home in Chile."

The Chilean sailors took him to the crew's quarters, fed him and dried his clothes He congratulated himself on his good fortune until he sensed the engines stopping. "What now?" he anxiously queried from the crew.

It appeared the Chilean Captain wasn't prepared to take him to South America.

He ordered Helmut into a small boat and delivered him to a Swedish ship bound for Stockholm.

"Yes! My luck's in," thought Helmut, "Internment in neutral Sweden. Just the job, I can live with that."

He gleefully spent the next few days planning his future away from hostilities.

Unfortunately for him, whilst he slept, the ship developed engine trouble and she docked in German-occupied Copenhagen.

Returned to submarines, he was reconciled to the fact that he would spend the rest of the war dodging allied warships and planes, all of them intent on denying him his inheritance.

But the best was yet to come. As he blundered through the latter part of the war his reputation as a jinx became a sick joke amongst U-boat crews. A series of minor mishaps appeared to plague the crafts he sailed in. Some Captains refused to take him when he was drafted to their boats. On one occasion, unable to find a Captain willing to give him a berth on a sub he was drafted to a boom defence boat. The duties of the craft entailed towing an anti-submarine net across the harbour mouth. His boom boat was relocating the net after the passage of a warship when they entangled a submerged U-boat.

The net was wrecked, the U-boat's propellers were damaged, but the final humiliation was that the boom defence boat sank, blocking the harbour for a number of days. Poor Helmut took the brunt of sailors' jokes until only a shore establishment would give him sanctuary. However, his *pièce de résistance* came when the Germans finally surrendered. He was drafted to a shore gang under the auspices of an English Captain. Helmut giggled at this stage of the story and explained what tickled him. He was sure that if the English Captain had only spoken German he too would have refused to employ him, when the other Germans explained their nervousness at having Helmut working with them.

Their final act of the war was to moor the U-boats as they came into port after surfacing and surrendering. Darkness was just falling. They were hauling one U-boat alongside another. Nobody noticed a floating mine in between the two craft. As they came together the mine exploded, sinking the U-boats in an essential part of the docks. Fortunately, nobody was below in the subs at the time of the explosion. Helmut and his comrades only suffered minor injuries but did have to swim for their lives. He reckoned he spent so much time swimming fully clothed that he felt naked when he went to a swimming pool wearing only a costume.

Despite his brushes with death Helmut was grateful for some of his wartime experiences. He did learn to cook after a fashion in the cramped galleys of the U-boats and other Navy craft and shore establishments he served in.

But he considered his greatest achievement was the creation of a haggis, and his finest recollection of the war was the Burns Night supper in Scotland. Hence, the monthly Scottish ritual in 'Helmut's Place'.

After this disaster he was shipped to England to help in the reconstruction. That is when he was engaged on the canals and met Betty, his wife-to-be.

In 1946 his brother arrived home from another prison camp, when he married his childhood sweetheart Inge. Throughout the war she had been a cook for some of the highest-ranking German officers, gaining fantastic culinary experience.

Together they rebuilt 'Helmut's Place,' featuring the ornately tiled stove. When the brother died Helmut gained his rightful inheritance. His sister-in-law remained as chief cook with Betty assisting.

What a story! Helmut finished relating the final chapter of his wartime career. I am eternally grateful that I was given the opportunity to know this couple. Were Helmut's wartime stories true or were they a figment of his imagination? He did have one eye missing and he definitely walked with a limp. He did have German Army, Navy, and Submarine service hats hanging in the pub over photographs of him in the full appropriate uniforms. I don't think the validity of his experiences mattered. They were definitely good entertainment when related by Helmut.

Unfortunately I lost touch with the couple. I went back years later but they were long gone. The pub had been modernised, the name changed and it was being run by new owners.

Chapter Eight
Problems to be sorted

ONE OF 'ARRY'S great-uncles was dying. He was in his late nineties and had lived and worked on the waterways all his life. It seems this man was the only relative 'Arry liked. I suspected there was a cash inheritance in the offing when 'Arry approached me.

"I believe you are going to a meeting over in Yorkshire, eh, pal?"

How he knew my business astounded me, but that was 'Arry.

"Yes, I am, 'Arry. I shall be over there for a week or so doing a string of meetings. Then I'm on a course, what's your problem?"

"I have an old great-uncle, he lives over there. I've heard he is due to pop his clogs, any chance of you nipping in to see him?" He thrust a piece of dirty paper into my hand with an address scrawled across it.

He was some lad, was 'Arry. He talked as if Yorkshire was a couple of miles in diameter. I didn't respond but it didn't deter 'Arry; he carried on, "You can let me know if it's worth me going over there. I'll have to be on hand when he goes or those bloody hungry relatives of mine will strip the place within minutes."

'Arry took it for granted that I would comply with his request, but I had already made up my mind – sod 'Arry, the mercenary bugger. There was no way I was being a spy for him. I left him with a vague promise of going "if I have time."

I was in Yorkshire for nearly a week. On the third day I was having a meeting with John, one of the personnel managers, a good very caring man. While we were discussing mundane items his secretary interrupted us with an apology. "I've just had a phone call from the section inspector. He's just seen the local doctor. Old Bob is on his last legs and he wants to see you urgently."

John rubbed his chin. "I'll have to go and see him, he's the last of the old canal company employees. He has been on canals all his life, way before they were nationalised. Do you mind delaying the meeting until I sort this out?"

I replied with a request: "Not at all, in fact I wouldn't mind coming with you. I would like to see the old boy."

He appeared grateful and accepted my suggestion immediately.

We arrived at the cottage and were admitted by a scrawny-looking woman. The downstairs rooms were crowded with people. They turned out to be Old Bob's relatives, the manager ascertained by some discreet questioning. The local doctor was also present; the manager knew him and they shook hands. I was introduced as Bob's union representative.

He informed us, "I don't know how the old man is still alive, by rights he should have been dead hours ago. To be honest that's why I'm still here."

He showed us upstairs to Bob's bedroom. The old boy was propped up in bed by a heap of pillows. The curtains were drawn and his pale face was illuminated by the light of a single candle. John whispered, "Bob was born in the cottage and has lived here all his life. He has not permitted the company to modernise it in any way, hence the candle for lighting."

On Bob's head was one of those Wee Willy Winky nightcaps, with a long tassel dangling to one side of his gaunt face. His eyes flickered open when the sound of our entry disturbed him. A skeletal hand emerged from beneath the covers and he gestured for us to come closer. We moved together, edging near to his bed. His breath was rasping but he managed to say, "Come closer."

My companion leaned over him. Bob whispered something I could not distinguish. I heard the personnel manager reply. "That's all right, Bob. I will sort that out – you know you can trust me."

The old man appeared satisfied, slumped back onto the pillows, let out a long sigh and died.

The doctor examined him and declared him dead. The manager removed a large manila envelope off the dressing table at the doctor's instruction, and we climbed down the narrow stairs. At the bottom of the stairs we walked into the crowd of his relatives crushed into the narrow hallway. From there the doctor broke the news of Old Bob's death. The manager and I left in the car, and we were heading back to Leeds when I asked him, "Do you mind telling me, what did Bob say to you just before he died?"

He replied thoughtfully, "It's a bit complicated and I'll have to check on it when I get back to the office and look in the records.

"It appears that Bob is entitled to a free coffin under an old canal agreement. That is what he was making sure he got before he died. Would you believe that? The old boy stayed alive until I assured him he would get his entitlement," he shook his head.

Suddenly he pulled the car to a halt, took the envelope out of his briefcase and opened it carefully. It contained a very fancy sheet of manuscript. He scanned through it then informed me with a smile, "Bloody hell, this is going to cause some commotion. Under his agreement the coffin has to be made by the canal workshops. I can't wait to tell the manager the good news. We will have to honour it. Imagine if the papers got hold of it if we had refused his last request?"

From his office I completed a series of meetings around the area, sleeping in a different hotel every night for nearly a week. When I arrived back at the office for another meeting I called in the office to be informed by the receptionist that it was Old Bob's funeral. All the office staff were attending and the meeting I had previously arranged was postponed until the afternoon.

Being at a loose end I decided to attend the funeral too, when one of the local drivers offered to take me. We arrived at the cottage to witness an extraordinary sight. The hearse was parked directly in front of the cottage containing nothing but wreaths and flowers. Next in line was a canal company truck with a huge coffin located on the rear. Behind that was a mobile crane, following that was a limousine containing six elderly men. After them was a single-decker bus full to capacity with canal employees. A string of assorted vehicles completed the convoy. I spotted the personnel manager on the pavement organising things. The funeral cortège moved off and he leapt into the limousine. The vehicle I travelled in was the last in the very long line.

We had to park a considerable distance from the prepared grave, so when I arrived the funeral was well underway. The mobile crane had lifted the coffin off the truck and had it suspended over the open grave. This was the first time I had the opportunity to see it in all its glory. Except for the usual coffin shape it did not resemble any I had ever seen. It was manufactured from the same material as lock gates, the seams were sealed with pitch and the handles were of cast iron. It was a wonderful piece of canal workshop ingenuity and a credit to the lads who had constructed it

The minister was just completing saying the "ashes to ashes dust to dust" bit as the coffin was lowered into the grave by the crane.

When I met up with the personnel manager in the afternoon he explained that Bob had chosen as his pall bearers his old mates, and not one of them was under eighty. There was no chance of them lifting the coffin. The funeral director had refused to carry the enormous coffin in his hearse because of the dimensions and the weight.

The funeral looked like turning into a disaster so he had come up with the best solution in the circumstances. He also told me, as it was a company cottage the property manager had visited to inspect the building. When he arrived it was entirely empty, stripped to the last item by his descendants when Bob was taken to the mortuary.

I had the vision of the old boy in maybe a hundred years wearing his Wee Willy Winky hat, his body still intact and worm-free in its oak coffin. He would have a smile of satisfaction on his face because he had received his entitlement, and Old Bob was the last one to do so. There was only one problem I could foresee. Come the day when the dead rose up the poor old boy would miss out. There was no way Bob would break out of that workshop-manufactured coffin. But a couple of centuries on it could be similar to the discovery of the intact mummies in Egypt. Who knows where Bob's body would be displayed in future? Maybe in a museum in Cairo, alongside the Pharaoh, Tutankhamen?

When I eventually returned to my home territory and confronted 'Arry he was not that pleased. Bob was his great-uncle and his relatives had beaten 'Arry to the loot. Diplomatic relations were severed by 'Arry until one of his old aunties was heard to have a rattle in her chest. The news spread around the country like wildfire, transmitted on the towpath telegraph. The vultures gathered from far and wide. 'Arry made sure he never missed out on this occasion. He was sat at the end of her bed when she gave her final gasp with his eyes firmly fixed on her jewellery box and a set of false teeth she had recently inherited from yet another member of the family.

Another day another problem, such was the life of an elected union representative in the waterways industry.

Though my primary employment was as a lock-keeper, I spent most of my time as the elected representative negotiating and sorting out disputes in the canals of Northern England.

It was about nine o'clock in the morning when the phone rang and I received a call requesting my services.

It had been a great weekend – the previous night in particular – a family party, plenty of pop and a good old knees-up on Sunday. It was not the best night for a shindig with having to work the following day and I was really paying the penalty for it. My head throbbed, my mouth tasted like yuk. I tenderly rubbed my stomach region. My guts didn't feel too good either, as they gurgled and groaned indicating a touch of Gandhi's revenge. Bloody curry! I cursed my stupidity for partaking of the Eastern Time bomb. That would be the last time I'd have one of the high-octane Vindaloos from the Star of India.

The canal supervisor, Pontius Pilot – a bit of a creep even for management – was the caller. He did not return my weak "Hello!" There was no "Good morning!", not even a "How do you do?", when he recognised my voice on the phone.

The miserable bugger immediately went into moan mode.

His first words to me were: "You'd best get down to that gang of nutters on the piling, they're at it again. The daft sod's been on the blower, babbling on about something dangerous in the water where they're working."

Without naming him I knew he was referring to 'Arry, a temporary addition to the gang of three working together piling the canal banks. The lads had been complaining to the supervisor by way of the radio.

He continued, "He's shouting about danger money, barmy bugger. Silly sod is only with the gang for a fortnight while Tommy's away. Biggest mistake I ever made putting 'Arry with them. If only there had been someone else that would work with the silly sods. Ah! But you know how it is? There's nowt there to cause them problems. I was with them yesterday. Really glad they were to get a Sunday in, lots of the old double time. The grabbin' sods! Bloody marvellous the way problems always come up on a weekend, eh?"

There was no need for me to contribute to the conversation. The supervisor loudly, and rapidly, did all the talking. I slumped against the wall, with the phone held about three inches from my aching head, listening to him droning on and on.

Loud warnings evolved from my nether regions as the Indians exacted their revenge on me for the sins of the British Empire.

"You know what 'Arry's like for overtime? The job's going great, soft bottom, easy driving. They should finish this length ahead of time. Finish ahead of bloody time? That'll be a soddin' miracle. Get down and have a word with them will you? I wash my hands of those buggers, I really do!"

Here he went again. I'm sure he was a reincarnation of that Roman fella in the bible. Well, never mind that. Bugger me, though, he didn't half go on.

The use of the description 'soft bottom' reminded me I had a problem of my own looming. Desperately I pinched the cheeks of my pulsating buttocks together.

A slight pleading tone entered his voice. "You know I can't pay bloody danger money, pal. They will go off their head in the top office if this job isn't finished on time. They're on about bringing contractors anyway to do the next job."

Danger! Danger! I winced – he didn't know what danger was.

He was lucky he was about five miles away on the end of the phone instead of standing behind me. That would be real danger, matey.

He cajoled, "If you go down right away and have a word? I won't tell the boss about them stopping the job."

He spoke with hardly a pause, as if unburdening himself in a confessional.

Realising he had made promises about unreachable targets to his bosses made me feel slightly better. He was always trying to ingratiate himself with top brass, hoping to further his career at the expense of the men.

I knew there was no real urgency. I could take my time sorting out the problem. He would, typically, keep clear until the matter was resolved.

"Where are they working now?" I asked wearily.

"Oh, Lord, no!" I protested to my guardian angel as another uncontrollable explosion burst from my posterior. "Not again," I implored, silently.

The supervisor paused in his diatribe and questioned, "Eh! Eh! What did you say? Is that a ship blowing I hear? I didn't know there is anything booked for the lock at this time?"

Weakly hanging onto the windowsill with my teeth, I didn't bother enlightening him as to the origin of the sound.

It was imperative that I finished this conversation immediately. I would be in real trouble if I didn't get to the bog right away.

I interrupted him for the first time by repeating my request for the location of the piling gang and transport to get there.

"By the power station," he advised. "They're doing the towpath side, you know where I mean? Take Tony's van, he's on holiday today. The spare keys are with the Fixer. He should be there unloading his truck. You can park by the pub, it's right alongside the job."

My heart sank as I agreed to visit the site. Bloody hell, they were working by a pub. Fancy allowing that lot within ten miles of a boozer, never mind bloody near inside it.

I couldn't delay any longer. Slamming the phone down after agreeing to anything, I raced to the bog. Thank you Lord, it was not occupied. I made it just in time.

In a flash it was all over. I sat completely drained, experiencing the same feeling women must have after giving birth. Weakness, relief, and a feeling of sudden emptiness – but one exception thank goodness, nothing to cuddle.

A few minutes elapsed as I recuperated from my traumatic purging. I felt a lot better and able to face the world. My mind began to function again as I gave thought to the immediate problems.

The enormity of the task ahead daunted me – most probably another no-win situation created by 'Arry and Co.

Spare me. I could have done without a session with him and his cronies on a Monday, especially feeling knackered as I did. I reckoned this would be the umpteenth time I'd sorted out problems in the week 'Arry had been with them. I knew when the Pilot told me 'Arry was going to work with the other two head cases that it would be a disaster.

Would my misfortunes of this day never end, I complained to the empty toilet roll holder.

Destruction!

The van wouldn't start.

The truck driver had tried to start the van and failed. He expertly diagnosed a flat battery.

The Fixer immediately took charge and volunteered to sort things out.

"No problem, we'll start the van by towing it with the supply truck," he promised. "Piece of cake – quick snatch with the truck and you'll be away. It's the frost you see, these vans are always temperamental when it's frosty."

He borrowed a chain from a tractor driver working in the field nearby as there were no towropes available. It was not a good substitute but he was an experienced driver and assured me it would be OK. I naively believed him.

He handed me a bunch of keys and I took up the driver's position in the van. One of the canal men, Dreadnought, a dozy bugger, stood by to signal him when I was ready. From his position in the cab the Fixer couldn't see me because the van was so close behind the high truck, entirely owing to the short chain we were using.

Being unfamiliar with this particular vehicle I was searching for the ignition.

"Ah!" I said. "Right, here we go," as I found the location for the key.

Before I could actually put the key into the slot to unlock the steering, before I was able to actually release the handbrake, the canal-man assumed I was ready and signalled the truck driver to begin the operation.

The Fixer, a brilliant driver, to quote his own description of himself, started off much too fast. The truck leapt forward like a catapulted jet on an aircraft carrier, whipping the chain tight and twanging like a guitar string.

The van made an initial lurch forward then came to a grinding stop.

I sat incredulously, the keys still in my hand, watching a rear view of the truck, dragging a large portion of the front of the van behind it, shooting off down the towpath. The bright spark of a driver had only attached the chain to something not conducive to towing.

The van, the pride and joy of Tony, the relief foreman whom we called 'Smile-a-While', and his first new company vehicle, was half-wrecked. With trepidation, I climbed out of the driving seat to examine the damage. Then with a sinking heart I noticed Tony. The very same Tony allegedly on holiday.

He stood at his garage door, his mouth hanging open in astonishment. He was carrying the van battery he had been charging overnight...

Tony was aptly nicknamed. While the rest of the onlookers and ne'er-do-wells were falling about laughing he didn't even smile, not once. Oh shit! No sense of humour, some people. If only they would relax more and see the funny side of life. What a worrier, he'd finish up with ulcers, no doubt about it, if he didn't change his ways.

So... I filled in a sheaf of official forms. Took some Alka Seltzer and two or three Diacalms and had a bit of a lie down in a dark place. It was nearly eleven o'clock.

The useless truck driver, divorcing himself of all responsibility relating to the wrecked van, reluctantly agreed to drive me to the location of the piling gang.

He was not very familiar with that particular location. Foolishly I offered to guide him. Handicapped by my unreliable navigation and contradictory advice, we got lost.

The nearest he could finally get me to the site was on the wrong side of the canal opposite the piling barge. There I was evicted when he refused to spend any more time chauffeuring me about.

"If only you hadn't buggered up Tony's van," he admonished me as he dropped me off.

As he pulled away I asked him tentatively about getting me back to base after the meeting with the piling gang.

The driver, who had changed from being a good mate of mine first thing this morning to being sick of the sight of yours truly, was barely communicating with me.

He advised me to find my own way home or words to that effect.

The towpath terminated at the parked crane. A stack of gear, obviously set out for the job, was clearly visible from my position on the opposite bank.

A steel pile, half driven, still capped by the pile driver, remained suspended from the jib. The compressor, aimlessly generating air power, throbbed away ceaselessly. Big Al's crane, the cab door hooked open, revealed an empty driver's seat and innumerable levers and pedals.

The machine, deficient of an operator, stood idle like a redundant colossus poised over the towpath. Of the crew Dickey, 'Arry and Big Al there was no sign. Nobody responded to my shouts of "Hello, is there anybody there?"

Touch of the *Marie Celeste* this, I fanaticised. Wouldn't life be great if that were true? To get rid of my three biggest problems in one go would be better than winning the pools.

But inwardly I knew the gods would not be so kind as to rid me of the tiresome trio.

I noticed the accommodation boat containing their mess facilities moored further up the canal by the lock house. Friendly smoke feathered from the steel chimney pipe, signalling occupation.

Checking the time on my watch – yes, it was still dinner hour – I wandered along the path looking forward to a brew, certain they would be in the boat having their sandwiches.

I arrived to find it also deserted.

The door was open, and a kettle boiled merrily on the coal stove. I stood for a while scratching my head and wondering what to do next, inwardly berating them for causing me such damn problems when I had a hangover.

There was a noise behind me. I turned, a smile of greeting on my face, expecting to see the ugly mugs of the gang of three.

No such luck. This, I thought, was not one of my better days. Emerging from the cottage was the lock-keeper's wife, a small suitcase in one hand and an umbrella in the other.

I knew the lady from past encounters. To describe her as a lady does the female emancipation cause an injustice. She was well and truly emancipated. In fact it was her poor husband who should start a men's lib organisation.

Danny's wife, twenty years younger than him, was quite presentable at first glance. A petite lady, sporting long blonde hair and dressed immaculately. Believe me when I tell you her looks were only a disguise to lull unsuspecting people – especially men – into a false sense of security.

I once heard her described as a Venus fly-trap. 'Mrs. Jekyll' would have been a more appropriate description of this lady.

Her husband Danny, an ex-Liverpool Irish seaman, was nick-named 'Sugar Daddy' but not to his face. A great bear of a man, he had an ongoing problem with alcohol. Some said it was her that had driven him to it.

Consequently, I had been called in to represent him on a number of occasions when he found himself on disciplinary hearings because of his drinking habits. Despite these bouts, he was very popular with the customers and boaters. They were usually the culprits, guilty of encouraging him to drink as a reward for services rendered.

Danny, when sober, was an exceptionally good worker, and a nice man to boot. But when he imbibed the demon drink, look out! Fortunately for him the management knew this and took it into consideration when he occasionally lapsed.

Yet whenever I got him another chance by pleading mitigating circumstances, his wife seemed to hate me more and more. One of his mates told me she wanted him to get the sack so they could move back to live near her mother in Newcastle, her birthplace.

"Looking for the deadbeats?" she inquired with a sneering tone in her voice. "Looking for our little union members, are we?" she continued, as if she was addressing a child.

I didn't reply. I knew to my cost not to tangle with this particular vixen, especially when suffering a bad head.

"You didn't expect them to be working, did you? Lazy buggers!"

She pointed her umbrella towards the pub.

"It's gone opening time, you see? They're all down there, swilling ale. Lazy good-for-nothing so and so's. I'd sack the lot of them if I had my way."

I couldn't have her impugning the characters of my members. I ventured a reply, "Oh yes, and who would do all the work if you sacked them?" Under my breath I added, "You silly cow."

"I'd hire a load of monkeys. They'd be less trouble and far better looking than them three lazy sods. And you call me a 'silly cow' again and I'll sort you out, see if I don't."

She advanced a step. I retreated two steps.

"If my good-for-nothing husband is with them, you can tell him from me I've chucked his dinner to the dog. I'm off to me mother's so he needn't bother coming home. An' I don't know if and when I will be back. I've locked all the doors and he hasn't got a key. Sod him and his booze. Let him stay with his mates, he seems to prefer their company to mine. See if I care!"

Stupid me, would I never learn? My brain was just not functioning. I muttered again under my breath, "Bloody hell, Missus, I don't blame him. I'd sooner be in the company of a cobra than you."

This was a near-fatal mistake on my part. She must have been able to hear a pin drop at about a hundred yards. She certainly heard my muttered remarks.

Before I could take evasive action she rapidly advanced and landed a smart blow across my head with her rolled umbrella. She was only tiny but packed a mean wallop.

"Cobra, am I? Cobra? You, you cheeky sod! I'll 'cobra' you. All you foul-mouthed seaman are as bad as each other."

Slightly stunned I protected my head with a briefcase which I carried to make me appear more official. At this moment it was more appreciated than a suit of armour was by the knights of old.

My improvised head protector thwarted her next violent attack. Like a trained gladiator she switched the direction of her blow in mid air and cracked me across the shoulder.

"Bloody hell, Missus, that hurt!"

My battered body conceded defeat. I'd had enough of this. Good job she wasn't wielding a bloody sabre.

Anticipating another vicious blow I beat a hasty retreat, back stepping towards the pub. It was only when I calculated I had established a safe distance between myself and the mad witch that I stopped. The space gained between me and the psychopathic female gave me courage to remonstrate with her.

Nursing my doubly aching head I shouted, "You're a nutcase, you are, Missus. No wonder your poor bloody husband goes on the piss. I would myself if I had to come home to you every night. You bloody dragon."

Ha! That told her. I congratulated myself. I'd wanted to tell her a thing or two for ages but never got the chance.

Much to my chagrin my hurled insults landed on stony ground.

Totally ignoring me, she slammed the garden gate and flounced off towards the stop as a bus approached.

It was most probably her need to catch the bus that saved my miserable life.

I continued on my way apprehensively towards the pub.

"Psss!" A noise emitted from inside the derelict stables. I moved closer to investigate. A whispered voice, hard to define, spoke to me. I didn't fancy going any nearer and stood at the broken door warily avoiding entering the darkness.

The slurred voice, more audible now, questioned me.

"Is that you, pal? Has she gone? Do us a favour, will you? Make sure my missus has got on that bus."

The Liverpool accent gave me the clue to the hidden speaker.

"Is that you, Dan? What are you doing in this dump?"

"Pal, don't mess about. Is she gone or what? You know what she's like when I've 'ad a bevy!" Danny pleaded.

I looked back towards the road running alongside the lock cottage. There was nothing in sight – of the bus and of his wife there was no sign.

"Ah! You can come out, Dan. All clear – she's long gone," I assured him. Muttering curses, bangs and crashes issued from the interior until he staggered out of the disused stables.

What a mess he was in. Evidently he had been on a real binge. His forehead, displaying a huge gash, was covered in dried blood. The knees of his trousers, usually neatly creased, were torn and muddy – in fact, he looked a real disaster.

I gave his wife credit for one thing. When Danny was sober he was always turned out in pristine condition.

He nearly fell as he took some unsteady steps towards me. I rushed forward to support him but he brushed me away and sat down with a soft thump. He landed in a large heap of dog dirt.

"I'll be all right, pal, if I can just get up to the house an' get me 'ead down for a bit."

He scrabbled about. His legs threshed, vainly seeking purchase as he tried to stand up.

"Well, Dan. I've got some good news and some bad news for you," I said, trying to cheer him up.

"Your Missus has buggered off and left you, maybe for ever. That's the good news. The bad news is she's locked all the doors an' took the keys with her. Oh! By the way your dog's ate your dinner," I added this little gem so as he wouldn't worry about his favourite pet having nothing to eat.

He ceased trying to stand and took a half-pint bottle of gin from his pocket, offering it up to me.

Although I like a drink I declined on this occasion. I could have used a bracer after last night's session but it was gin. This liquor has a really depressing effect on my nature.

"Sod her, sod her mother. Sod the lot of them!" Danny cursed all and sundry.

To encourage him to take out his aggression on thin air I urged, "That's the business, Dan, make 'em 'ave it."

Having dealt with a number of drunks in my seagoing career I know it is far better to humour them than to attempt to reason.

Especially drunks named Danny who have Irish ancestry and the stature of a Grizzly Bear.

Then he started to cry. I couldn't cope with this, a whingeing bloody man. Making a tremendous effort he staggered to his feet. I slipped up and moved towards him offering a steadying hand. Before I could dodge aside he flung his arms around my neck weeping buckets full about his lost love.

The dog and his wife have similar names. Presuming he meant his dog as nobody could surely love his bitch of a wife, I said, "It's all right, Dan, I've told you the dog's been fed, so don't worry."

This didn't appear to pacify him as he set off into another series of wails, vows of love, and pleas. Betty or Betsy come back to me. I wasn't quite sure who he was appealing to.

This situation was becoming most embarrassing. The smell of the amassed dog doings adhering to him made my already fragile stomach feel extremely nauseous. An elderly lady with a pushchair remarked as she passed, "It shouldn't be allowed! Drunken queers kissing and suchlike in public."

She covered the child's head with a blanket to shield him from the appalling scene. "I shall call the Police and complain about such goings on," she threatened.

Vainly I tried to disentangle myself from Danny's embrace, while protesting my innocence to the lady. She was evidently not convinced and continued on her way, presumably to find a copper.

The wailing for the return of Betty or Betsy succeeded. The first I knew of her return was when she grabbed me by the trouser leg with her teeth. Thinking I was attacking her beloved master, the faithful dog was prepared to defend him with her life.

Conjuring up the last remnants of my strength I made a supreme effort and pushed Danny away from me

When we become disentangled he reeled towards the water threatening to end it all.

I pleaded with him not to do it, whilst trying to fight the dog off. He ignored my pleas and leapt into the canal, landing in about two foot of water inches from the bank. He stood for a moment swaying from side to side. It must have gradually dawned on his booze-besotted mind that he hadn't passed on to the great hereafter.

He lifted the gin bottle to his lips and celebrated his brush with death in the traditional seaman's way.

I was at my wits' end, beating the dog over the head with my briefcase to no avail. Eventually the dog succeeded in severing a large piece of my new trousers. She paused from attacking me for a moment to savagely shake her trophy to death.

The release of her hold on my leg gave me a chance to bolt for the sanctuary of the stable.

I didn't make it. The dog, an Alsatian-Rottweiler cross, caught me and pinned me up against the wall, paws on my shoulders and snarling face inches from my throat.

I prayed, 'Won't someone please help!' as my past life flashed in front of me.

Thank heaven. My prayers were answered, and salvation appeared in the guise of two members of the piling gang coming from the direction of the pub – 'Arry and The Fumigator.

As was the custom on waterways, nearly all employees had at least one nickname.

Dickey David Trubshaw was nicknamed 'the Fumigator', derived from his initials. DDT. His mates refered to him as 'DD'. He was another great poacher, always keeping himself and his mates supplied with game. Like 'Arry he spent the first and last part of the working day either setting or clearing his snares. He always carried a shotgun to work for big game hunting. Another ex-boat man, a distant relative of 'Arry, he was unable to read or write either. When 'Arry and DD joined forces, they were a formidable duo but fortunately this rarely happened as they worked in different sections.

The Fumigator, who had a way with animals, let out a piercing whistle. The slavering hound immediately released me and bounded over to him, where she sat to his order wagging her tail like a meek puppy.

He greeted me as I sorrowfully examined my torn trousers and the rest of my mud-stained clothes before wandering over to where Danny was paddling in the canal. The Fumigator chatted to him as if a man standing fully clothed in the water was normality.

There was no sign of Big Al, the third member of the contingent and the only member of the trio who could read and write..

The pair exchanged a few pleasantries and DD remarked in a rather crude way how unpleasant his colleague smelled covered in dog muck

I don't believe Danny realised how obnoxious his fragrance was until it was pointed out to him in no uncertain way.

DD's criticism of his appearance gradually penetrated his befuddled brain. The usually fastidious man was appalled at the loathsome coating that plastered him. He got a whiff of the foul smell permeating from his bedraggled clothes and threw up.

He started sobering instantly, casting the gin bottle far across the canal. Shuddering with disgust he began stripping off his contaminated clothing. When he was almost naked he commenced splashing in the weed-covered canal in an effort to rid himself of the noxious stuff.

Passing boaters and walkers were astounded at the sight of their favourite lock-keeper behaving in such a peculiar manner. The temperature was near zero, and it was not the season for canal bathing.

Approaching in the distance was the lady with the pushchair accompanied by a man in an official-looking uniform.

The Fumigator advised Danny to come ashore before he caught that *hippofermia whatsit,* and was got by them Pirahny things.

If I had been taking proper notice of his warnings instead of being concerned about my appearance I would have picked up the clue that instigated my being called to the site.

Danny now appeared almost sober. With the assistance of the Fumigator he scrambled out of the canal and made a beeline for the stables.

Big Al appeared from the direction of the road. He nipped over to me ahead of the other two.

"I've been waiting hours for you up the road, where've you been?" he admonished me. He didn't wait for an answer. "Er, er. I need to 'av a word, understand? I need to speak with you on our own without the other two." His voice dropped to a whisper as they came closer. Al put his finger to his lips in a pantomime gesture indicating secrecy.

Very intriguing – a split among the terrible trio.

The lady with the pushchair arrived.

"That's one of them," she pointed an accusing finger at me. "Should be locked up, behaving like that in front of decent people. Go on constable, do your duty."

The man in uniform was not a real policeman. It was Kojak, the waterways security man. My luck was changing for the better. I knew it must, some time. Kojak was also one of my union members.

Not quite understanding the situation, but I suppose having faith in me, he played along with the lady's misconception that he was a copper.

The guy deserved an Oscar for his performance as he lay down the law. He thanked the lady for her assistance and advised her to go on her way as he would be dealing with this matter most severely.

She trundled her pram away, still mumbling about depraved Britain, complaining that she would have expected Margaret Thatcher and Mrs Whitehouse to have sorted it all out by now.

Her removal from the scene made life easier. When the concerned lady was out of earshot, Kojak burst into laughter.

"Now then! Now then! What's going on 'ere? What's all this I hear about vice and corruption on the Queen's towpath?" he demanded, in a mock policeman's voice.

Big Al was pulling at my arm, urgently reminding me of his

need to talk to me alone.

The Fumigator and 'Arry, the worse for drink, were demanding danger money for working in the canal.

Sugar Daddy was shouting from the stables that he was freezing to death. His stupid dog, who five minutes ago had been trying her best to kill me, now decided that my Moroccan goatskin briefcase was her long-lost mate.

Growling and whimpering in a most bizarre manner, Betsy began making passionate advances to the goatskinned replica of her dream dog.

Surrounded by chaos and problems I gaped in awe, watching the dog performing. My brain went into free fall but still had time to query – I didn't know bitches did that??? Must be the smell of the leather. Maybe that's what affected her Mistress Betty, when she set about me? They say the smell of leather evidently affects some females in different ways.

Whoa! I must stop this daydreaming and concentrate on the matters at hand. I shook my head to clear my bewildered brain.

After enduring the hubbub for a few more minutes my usual composure snapped.

"Right!" I shouted. "I've had enough of this. I've got a bloody awful headache. I want a cup of tea, and a sit down in a nice warm cabin. I'm going up to the boat and won't discuss anything until I get there."

I thanked the security man for his help, and told him I'd give him a ring to explain later when I'd sorted this lot out.

Knowing the people I was dealing with of old, he appreciated my situation and exited the scene still laughing.

One less to deal with.

The remaining four of us were making our way towards the boat, leaving the dog and briefcase to carry on their affair in private. The loss of the briefcase was a cheap price to pay to get rid of that daft mutt. A pitiful voice inquired from the stable: "What about me, lads, you can't leave me here!"

Sugar Daddy! Damn! I'd forgotten all about him. Poor sod would most probably get pneumonia.

The dog abandoned her affair with the briefcase, and raced

towards her master's voice. Another problem solved. I went back and retrieved Betsy's rejected lover – slightly battered and festooned in love bites and saliva, but still serviceable.

Big Al interceded, "Hang on there a bit, Dan, I'll bring you some gear from the boat. I won't be a minute. Don't go 'way!'"

I gave him a scornful look, thinking, "What a stupid thing to say, but that's big hearted Al."

We arrived at the boat. I settled down in its homely warm interior.

DDT started making a brew. Ah! This was the life, peace and quiet at last. I stretched my aching legs, extending my frostbitten toes tentatively closer to the hot stove.

Big Al rummaged in the locker for something to cover Sugar Daddy's near nakedness

'Arry started on about "bloody fish with razor-sharp teeth."

"Stop!" I gestured him to be quiet. "Just let's have a brew in peace and a couple of these tablets and you can tell me all your troubles."

'Arry sat down muttering and lit his foul-smelling pipe.

DDT served up a steaming brew of tea in a filthy mug tasting distinctly of diesel oil, but who cared?

I heard voices on the towpath. Peering around the door, I saw Sugar Daddy being led up to his cottage by his screwy wife. He was clothed in a long old-fashioned cycle cape, his grotesque apparel completely shrouding him except for his white legs protruding from the hemline like elephant's tusks.

She was affectionately holding his hand like a naughty child.

His mad wife was making sympathetic noises like "there, there", to him. I couldn't believe it – the size of him and he was as docile as a castrated bull under the crazy cow's command.

I could hear her blaming me and the deadly trio for his misbehaviour. Damn cheek.

She was also promising him how she would deal with us when she got the opportunity. She'd be lucky.

For two pins I thought I'd go over there and give her another piece of my mind.

We were all four of us crowded in the cabin door watching this extraordinary sight until she glared threateningly in our direction, then we all dived for cover inside.

Anyway, another problem partially solved but in abeyance for the future.

One more task to complete – the reason for me being here in the first place.

I sat back and invited them to tell me their problem.

'Arry, the worse for drink, held a Sunday newspaper in front of me and asked indignantly, "What do you think about that? And us poor sod's 'ave got to stand for that, it's not bloody right."

He tapped the newspaper with his dirty index finger. DDT, also half cut, nodded in agreement. He backed up 'Arry with comments like, "Them sods wouldn't stand for it in their nice warm bloody offices."

Big Al, unusually for him, was exceptionally quiet. When I looked at him for comment, he nodded towards the door indicating he would appreciate it if I went with him off the boat.

I looked down at the newspaper to determine what all the fuss was about. The main headline was concerning a transvestite, who was trying to raise the money for a sex change by offering to sell his redundant parts.

I wondered if they wanted me to help them donate their organs for cash. They were always dreaming up schemes to make money.

The mystery deepened. I really didn't want to get involved in this. I decided to accept Big Al's invitation to go with him in the hope he would throw some light on the problem. He appeared quite sober and was able to read and write. This fact had got to help.

I made an excuse to the other two.

"Just let me nip on the phone and get some advice about this and I'll be right back. You two stay here in case the Pilot turns up."

I pointed to Big Al, "You come with me and show me where the phone is."

Al grabbed the newspaper and followed me out of the boat. We made our way to the pub at his insistence to use the phone in there.

Before going ashore and risking another near-decapitation I

made sure there was no sign of Sugar Daddy's erratic wife. I gave the all-clear to Al and we furtively stepped off the boat. We had to pass the lock cottage to make our way down the towpath. As we proceeded we heard poor old Danny being chastised.

In between the crashes of hurled crockery and screams of abuse we detected Danny pleading for mercy. Al and I looked at each other and quickened our steps to a near run, both glad we were not the recipients of Betty's tender administrations. Ain't love wonderful?

"I suppose you lot are responsible for Sugar Daddy's predicament, been leading him astray again?" I remarked disapprovingly.

Al denied responsibility. "The last time I saw Danny was in the pub on Sunday night when we had a few pints after knocking off. He was with a gang of pleasure boaters when we left, having a great time. They were buying all his ale. Lucky sod! Honest, it's not down to us. I bet he's been out all night. No wonder his mis sus is mad with him."

I shook my head, "Will he never learn? I suppose I'll have to defend him yet again if this comes out."

Al assured me, "Don't worry, me old mate, nobody's been down here this morning. As long as he's okay for tomorrow, he'll be all right. We'll cover for him."

His optimism pleased me no end.

We arrived at the pub, one of my favourite kinds. It was a real old-fashioned boozer with lots of character, that thankfully had never been refurbished or modernised. Looking for a bit of privacy to discuss the problems we were directed into the empty snug by a barmaid. We pressed the bell and ordered a couple of pints from the red-faced landlord who appeared to have difficulty restraining giggles.

He didn't even have the courtesy to reply to our greeting, rushing out of the snug when we paid him.

Al remarked, "I wonder what's up with that ignorant bugger – usually it's hard to shut him up when we come in here."

I shrugged. "Maybe someone's just told him a joke or something. Who gives a damn?"

The owner of the alehouse was a fanatical angler and fishing tackle and memorabilia related to fishing crammed the place. Glass cases on all the walls displayed stuffed fish from every corner of the world.

I took a sip of my pint and invited Big Al to tell me all about it.

He unfolded the newspaper and indicated a small article in the bottom corner of the front page.

The story was all about the area they were piling. It seemed that the discharged water from the power station had raised the temperature of the canal water. A member of the caring public had released tropical fish into the water. They were not only surviving but thriving in the artificially-created tropical conditions.

"All very interesting but what has that to do with me?" I inquired. Big Al drew my attention to a glass display case containing a ferocious-looking fish with enormous teeth.

I read the inscription: "Piranha fish caught by George Simmons, the landlord of this public house, on an expedition up the Amazon in 1970."

I was still puzzled when Big Al decided to come clean and told the story.

On Monday mornings when they first arrived at work Al read aloud the Sunday papers to his mates. This was a practice they looked forward to with relish, especially stories containing lots of juicy bits that the Sundays are notorious for printing.

He read them the article regarding tropical fish in the canal where they were working. For added flavour he included in the list of fish released, the piranha – a fish they always talked about when in this particular pub because of its habit of stripping unwary travellers of their flesh. Al informed me the landlord relished describing in detail the time he was on the Amazon when he lost his wife to the fish. Gruesome sod. "But eh!" Al added in a whisper. "I haven't seen his missus since, you know?"

The Fumigator and 'Arry had recently also seen nature programmes about the eating habits of the piranha on the telly and the pictures.

After he read them the article they refused to stand in the water or even go near it to steady the piles as the job entailed.

Big Al saw a chance to get his own back for all the ridicule he'd had to endure because of the Italian army's conduct under Mussolini. He enjoyed his moment of triumph as he mocked them for their lack of courage.

To prove that Italians are braver than the English despite what happened in the war he decided to demonstrate that the job was safe. He valiantly dangled his welly-shod feet into the weed-covered water from the side of the piling barge.

What was cleverly concealed from the other two was the fact that he had roughly cut the toe out of one of the boots.

He invited them to come closer and watch as he courageously dared the fish to attack him by waggling his feet invitingly in the water. His mates were very impressed with his nerve. Nervously they edged forward to see his antics more clearly. It was then he sprang his trap.

They jumped back in alarm when he let out a shout of pain and rolled backwards into the boat. Horror was displayed on their faces as the apparently well-chewed welly was exposed.

Well this was it. This was what I was here for after suffering probably the worst day of my life.

I stared at Al in wide-eyed disbelief. I didn't know whether to laugh or cry. If by some miracle there were piranhas in the canal I could have cheerfully flung the three of them in and happily watched as they were torn to pieces.

While he was relating his story I detected muted laughter from behind the frosted glass screen of the booth. I thought I recognised a couple of these voices. Quietly leaving our table we went around the other side of the screen.

I was confronted by the pub landlord, 'Arry and the Fumigator.

On seeing Big Al standing behind me, their suppressed laughter exploded. They were practically on their knees convulsed with hysterical cackling.

The worst day in my union career really ended there. The landlord disclosed all after he stopped laughing.

After the welly incident the gullible duo rushed into the pub at opening time and there they cornered the landlord. Out of breath from the unaccustomed vigorous exercise they were barely able to speak, instead they excitedly pointed to the encased piranha. Eventually after gulping down a medicinal glass of rum the pair gushed out the tale of the killer fish in the canal.

They had a brilliant plan, they explained, which they would willingly share with the landlord to get some free ale. Knowing them of old he wouldn't agree until they disclosed the cunning part of their plot.

In a confidential whisper 'Arry assured the landlord that it wouldn't cost him personally a single penny.

The source of cash for their beer? This was the clever part, they revealed – the fishing fanatics that frequented the place. The anglers would be more than willing to reward them for such exclusive information on where and how to catch the rarest fish in British waters.

The schemers continued to disclose another well thought-out business plan, and this one almost topped the other for its simplicity and audacity.

They could even sell special bait that nobody else would supply – made from the chopped-up carcasses of the dead dogs and cats they hauled from the canal every day.

I'd got to take my hat off to these two. The clever monkeys were already being paid a special bonus for clearing dead animals from the cut and burying them.

Who needed education with brains like 'Arry and the Fumigator? They should have got some kind of award for recycling from the Green Party.

This scheme would have made a bloody fortune between the two of them, and the landlord of course.

Al wasn't interested when they put the plan to him. Poor sucker couldn't see a gift horse when it was offered, and serve him bloody right when he realised how much he was missing out on, they reckoned.

'Arry and his mate were virtually dancing with glee at their own ingenuity.

Although the landlord congratulated them on their business acumen he had to decline their offer of a fortune. He fortunately had a copy of the Sunday paper where they referred to piranhas.

On examining it he found they were not mentioned in the article. It took some time, but eventually he convinced them that it was impossible for piranhas to survive in this country. Eventually they accepted his word, only because he was acknowledged by all anglers to be the top expert on all types of fish.

The two mates were devastated when they realised that their opportunity to become millionaires had disappeared.

To exact their revenge on Big Al, the source of their misfortune, they enlisted the aid of the landlord in the planning and execution of this outlandish scheme.

The revenge entailed letting the poor sod spell out to me why the job was stopped because of him. Then he had to apologise to me for my wasted journey.

All this time 'Arry and DDT were concealed, listening to his explanation behind the screen with the landlord and barmaids of the pub.

What a bloody gang – and I'd still got to figure a way to get back home to my base.

Big Al was in a panic. I was on my way to the bus stop by the lock cottage when he caught up with me. His face registered dread.

"Pal, wait a mo'. Er... what are you going to tell Pontius Pilot about all this when you get back? He'll bloody well sack me if you tell him about this lark."

I stood for a while, my hand raised to my head as if giving deep thought to his problem. I was making him suffer considerable apprehension as a reward for his brilliant hoax that had gone wrong.

At last I said as I started walking away, "Got it, Al, don't you worry. Your old mate cracked it. I'll tell the Pilot I've sorted the problem out and you are all working normally."

His face broke into a beam of relief.

"But!" I added, "If he doesn't send you steel toe-capped thigh boots and armoured gauntlets in the morning you are going to stop the job again."

I eventually caught a bus that took me to a place, where I caught another bus which took me to another place, where I caught a train that took me to yet another place, where I only had to walk about five miles to get home.

But you had to laugh in this game or the lads would, sure as hell, drive you progressively and inexorably mad.

Chapter Nine
The Bridge

SPRING WAS HERE. The first boats of the season were beginning to move after the long winter's lay up The crews were refreshed by a couple of celebratory pints in the waterside pubs. Everyone I encountered was feeling great. The birds sang, the daffodils were out in full bloom. I was personally feeling on top of the world. This was the first time I was to swing this particular bridge. It was the longest bridge on the river and required a second man for safety reasons. Today I was to swing it without an expert regular driver being present.

"It can be a bit temperamental, so watch her. If you stick this bugger, the traffic will pile up for miles," the retiring bridge driver warned me. He thought for a moment and made me feel really confident by informing me, "Especially when it's a hot day."

He paused then added, "or frosty."

I was feeling quite confident before his advice. He exited much to my relief but popped back within seconds.

"Oh! The wind can be a bitch as well, so watch out, especially if it's blowing up river," he added, just to make me happy before finally departing for his well-earned rest.

My initial confidence was slightly shaken by now. Still, I'd done it ten times at least under his supervision. I was full of confidence, I assured myself. There was, however, another cloud on the horizon. As nobody else was available the dreaded 'Arry had been sent to act as second man on the road bridge I was operating. I had a sinking feeling in my stomach when he volunteered to be my second man on that Sunday. I overheard him chatting to the bus driver who was curious as to why he had opted for this particular bridge especially of a weekend. There was one much closer to where he lived.

"Double time, my old mate, and there's a pub opposite."

A nod was as good as a wink. I knew I had to keep an eye on 'Arry, who moved like quicksilver when ale was concerned.

What was worse was that this was the first time he had ever been involved in operating a bridge – why did it happen today, of all days? The Spring flowers appeared to fade as I faced the day with trepidation.

"Now, he doesn't have to do much," I consoled myself. "Even 'Arry can't cause me grief today, surely?"

He had virtually just to stand on the far end, away from the control cabin, and make sure the railway crossing type barriers were in place. This was purely a safety precaution as the barriers were automatic and I would operate them. Another small duty he had to carry out was to grease the far side wedges with a long turk's head brush when the bridge was in the 'off' position.

This was the only time this particular task could be carried out, when the wedges were exposed.

All was going well, and a feeling of relief enveloped me.

The apprehension I first felt when 'Arry was sent to assist me vanished as Spring worked its magic on my sun-starved body. A mixed flotilla of boats was approaching. I pressed the button, the warning alarms sounded, 'Arry importantly took up position at the far end, his turk's head brush at the ready.

He confidently waved to me. Road traffic stopped, I operated the barriers. No problems, thumbs up from 'Arry. I dropped the wedges and swung the bridge off successfully. Breathing a sigh of relief I felt unseen eyes watching my progress from the retired bridge keeper's house.

Boats passed through, passengers on every one cheerfully waving and calling to each other. Pedestrians waved excitedly, boaties reciprocated.

I noted a number of 'Arry's ex-boating friends' boats were amongst the flotilla.

"Be on their way to the boat club rally," I explained to a truck driver who had taken the opportunity to have a smoke and enjoy the scene. Gradually other motorists joined us, enjoying the spectacle and asking questions. One remarked admiringly, "How nice that the narrowboats are painted with flowers and castles."

I explained, "They are ex-boatmen and women; of course they live full time on the boats and are very proud of them."

A car on the far end was tooting his horn continually.

"That's nice, listen to the cars greeting the boats going through. I really like this job – you get to meet some great people," I informed the man smugly.

The driver thanked me for stopping him this morning. "I wouldn't have missed all this for the world, it's great."

This was a nice change for me. Usually everyone was in a hurry. I've had many a curse directed at me for swinging a bridge just as they approached. I was really enjoying this day, glad I volunteered to operate the bridge. All those tales I'd heard about irate motorists were a load of codswallop, most probably invented by the bridge drivers to keep others from taking the best jobs. It was definitely the Spring feeling that was responsible for people's happy moods today. The truck driver pointed out a horse on the far side, a young girl mounted on it.

"Must be nice, eh? Riding a horse on a lovely morning like this, something I've always wanted to do," the driver confessed longingly.

I sympathised with him, noted the last craft had passed through and returned to the control cabin. I swung the bridge on, relocated the wedges, lifted the barriers and relaxed in the armchair. Phew! I'd got through that first solo swing quite easily.

'Arry appeared at the door.

"All right, 'Arry?" I greeted him.

He looked a mite uneasy. I stood up, and a feeling of dread swept over me. I detected the ring of hooves on the bridge decking as a horse galloped past the doorway behind him.

"What's up?" I enquired hesitantly.

Quick as a flash he answered, "You've only gone an' hung some poor bugger's dog."

"What?" I collapsed back into the chair. Just then a man pushed passed 'Arry and approached me in a threatening manner.

"My poor Cuddles, I loved that dog. What are you going to do about it, you murderous swine?"

I looked through the window. There appeared to be some kind of problem on the far side. Traffic was not moving. It looked to me like a Mini was parked in the oncoming lane. The angry man grabbed me by the shoulder, marched me over to the window and pointed.

"There. There, you damned fool! Look! Will you? Just see what you've done?" To my horror I saw the focus of his anger. A small dog was hanging from the top of one of the safety barriers.

Chaos reigned as another person entered the cabin, closely followed by a young lady in riding gear. The young man, whom 'Arry identified as the owner of the Mini, threatened and swore at the young girl who promptly lashed at him with her riding crop. The dog man threatened and swore at me. 'Arry, observing I had the undivided attention of the enraged dog owner, furtively sneaked out and disappeared towards the pub opposite. I leapt to the button, and pressed the alarm.

The friendly truck driver of a few minutes ago popped an angry face in through the door.

"What the bloody hell's going on? I was just about to move off in my wagon when you sounded the bloody alarm for the barrier right in front of me. Another few inches and you would have hit the cab if you had dropped the bloody things. You're a bloody dangerous nutter. I've got a load to deliver and want to get back to Birmingham today. How long are you going to hold me up now? I hate these stupid bridges. They're on and off like a whore's drawers. I'm always getting stuck with them."

This was the very same man that minutes before had been enjoying the delay. He must have been a schizophrenic and prone to mood changes, I assumed, but tactfully kept my opinion to myself.

Oh dear! Maybe the tales about irate motorists were true after all. I started to explain with difficulty above the sound of the alarms that the road was blocked on the far end. A motorbike whizzed past. The angry driver backed out of the doorway to admit someone else. The local copper entered the cabin in time to witness the horsey girl and the Mini lad nearly coming to blows. He was no help, standing just inside the doorway grinning. I checked the road with difficulty and dropped the barriers.

"You mad cow!" the Mini lad berated her. "You and your bloody horse have wrecked my beautiful car."

The horsey girl replied in a scornful voice. "It's only a cheap old Mini, for goodness sake, who, drives Minis these days, anyway?"

Then more angrily she continued, "The point is, what are you going to do about my horse – he's run off!"

"Your horse, you mad bitch! My car is a very rare Mini Cooper, I'll have you know. I've just taken twelve months restoring it. It's my first time out..." he added tearfully, his shoulders slumped, the sad picture of utter despair. Then angrily he suddenly braced up and took a wild lunge towards the girl, arms outstretched as if to strangle her. The local copper stepped between them, blocked his charge, restrained him, and advised calm while he sorted the problem out.

I took the opportunity to dodge past the squabbling people, vacate the cabin, and rush across the bridge towards the scene of the dog's unfortunate demise. The horsey girl and the Mini lad, still arguing heatedly, followed. The local copper, and last but not least Cuddles' bereaved owner, trailed after us. I could hear the dog man accusing me of unspeakable murder in a loud whingeing voice.

I arrived to find the scene was quite a tourist attraction. Vehicles tailed back up the road as far as I could see. Rubbernecks stood about remarking about this and that, but particularly the main topic of conversation was the spectacle of the dog Cuddles. He now lay alongside the lowered barrier in the middle of the road, eyes bulging, tongue hanging out of his frothy mouth with his neck still tethered to the barrier. The local copper took control. Unhooking the dog, he passed it over to his distraught owner. He then organised us to push the Mini off the road after ordering the sightseers back to their vehicles.

When he had the traffic organised again we retired to the

bridge cabin for the inquiry, whereupon I raised the barriers for a second time. Looking out of the door to ascertain all was back to normal I was just in time to see a wagon passing at speed with the angry driver making V-signs at me from his cab. It amazed me how one small delay could turn an amiable person into a road rage fiend. Oh, well such were the benefits of being a bridge driver on a busy road, eh! And this was on a Sunday. My God, what if I had a problem at rush hour? I shuddered inwardly as I wondered if I had done the right thing volunteering for this job.

I rang the AA at the request of the Mini lad. Just as I hung up a local farmer contacted the copper on his mobile and told him he had found a saddled horse wandering near his property. He had it safely tied up in his paddock. Thank goodness.

I went to fetch 'Arry as a crucial witness at the insistence of the dog man. He was, as I guessed he would be, ensconced by the pub bar in the middle of his third pint. He was relating the events of the day with his wildly exaggerated interpretation to a crowd of wide-eyed American tourists. They were plying this really colourful Limey character with booze. I was just in time to hear 'Arry telling the sympathetic audience confidentially that I was only a learner bridge driver. He was trying his best to teach me, but was facing an uphill battle.

"He's not very bright, you see, hasn't had much edification," he explained as a way of excusing my misdemeanours on the bridge on that beautiful Spring morning.

I was taken prisoner by a huge American lady besporting an enormous strangely sculptured hat decorated with more flowers than the local park, who rebuked me for not paying attention to my very quaint superior.

The gigantic Yank pinned me to the bar, her huge mammaries thrust ahead of her like the stem fender on a tugboat either side of my head as she expressed her disapproval at my lack of respect for my knowledgeable associate. Although I was turning blue from the lack of oxygen, my nose embedded in the grand canyon smothered by her monstrous mountains of flesh, for some reason I had the sudden inexplicable desire for a Farley's Rusk and a good burping – until I realised I hadn't had my traditional Sunday roast yet.

"You should listen to your elders. That's the trouble with you young ones. It's the same in our country, you won't listen."

With a deft duck that would have put an acrobat to shame, I slipped under her menacing protrusions and cringed half in and out of the doorway making gestures at 'Arry. Every time I gestured to him he raised his glass in my direction and shouted, "Cheers, Scouse, me old pal."

The huge American lady was matching 'Arry pint for pint. Unused to the Irish brew she was soon well and truly sloshed, and she joined 'Arry in wishing me "Cheers, my old pal!" in her Mid-Western accent.

I eventually extracted him from the bar and persuaded the lady she would be better off in the pub. When after a few near disasters I got him back to the cabin, things had settled down. Thank goodness, the local copper had professionally chaired the impromptu inquiry and calmed everyone down. The two young antagonists were as far from each other as possible in the limited confines of the control cabin, warned, under the pain of arrest, to refrain from shouting abuse and threats at each other by the constable.

Poor old Cuddles, the silent witness, was laid out peacefully at rest on my armchair. His master stood by the chair stroking his curly hair, tears streaming down his face. The events leading to the fracas came to light as follows.

First to turn up when the barriers dropped was the girl on the horse. Second, parking behind her, the Mini arrived. When the boats passed through 'Arry shouted and waved to his mates. Though the horse became restless at 'Arry's antics it was still under control, the horsey girl attested.

"You see, I ride with the hunt. I am a very experienced rider, spending a great deal of my free time mounted."

The Mini lad, still angry, saw a chance to humiliate the girl by remarking in a sneering voice, "I bet you do."

The local copper kept them apart yet again.

The real trouble evidently started when the lad in the Mini spotted his girlfriend sunbathing on one of the luxury boats as it passed through the bridge. She had allegedly declined to ride in his Mini using the excuse she had to attend the Sunday church service. Despite the lad waving and shouting her name she pointedly ignored him. In frustration he tried attracting her attention by blowing the Mini horn repeatedly. It was then that the startled horse went berserk and kicked in the front of his Mini. When the front of the car was completely wrecked, with the horse's legs bleeding, the girl finally pacified her mount and although still nervous the horse settled down.

Arguments about insurance heatedly began with both sides blaming each other. The dog man having witnessed the occurrence offered some advice. He pointed out he was in the insurance business himself and the couple could have problems claiming. He did however offer to give evidence if they required. The lad handed him a note pad and pen. The dog man gave Cuddles' lead to 'Arry while he wrote his name and address. 'Arry remembered he had to do the greasing and tied the dog's lead to the barrier. The last craft passed through the bridge and I swung it back on. 'Arry forgot the dog – then I lifted the barrier and hanged poor Cuddles.

"Nice one, 'Arry, you have swung the lot onto me."

After giving his evidence 'Arry departed at speed again in the direction of the pub. The AA man arrived and took the Mini away on a car transport truck. The local copper exonerated me from blame. He then ran the dog man and stiffening corpse of Cuddles home. I took the girl in my van to the farm to recover her wayward mount.

The retired bridge keeper, the fund of all knowledge about the bridge, appeared and informed me with a satisfied grin on his face, "It ain't as easy as it appears, the life of a bridge driver, eh? You've had one day of it – I've had forty years. You ain't seen nothing yet."

He continued advising me about the contrary bridge. "Now then, let this be a warning to you. Never assume you have mastered this bitch – she's just like a woman. Just when you think you are in charge of her she will pull a stunt like today. She has been catching drivers out since the bloody thing was built."

THE BRIDGE

He settled down in the armchair he evidently missed since his retirement and began, "I remember when..."

I cut in before he related a string of woes and thanked him for his words of wisdom whilst wondering how I could get out of the job with dignity.

'Arry tottered out of the pub hours later and joined some of his friends on a boat tied up by the bridge. He was still aboard next morning and went straight to work from there. I finally made it home hours later to a ruined Sunday roast after experiencing one of the worst days of my life.

Only one good thing came out of that eventful day. About a month later the same Mini Cooper, fully restored again, pulled up and parked by the bridge. I couldn't believe what I saw next. The Mini lad and the horsey girl approached me hand in hand and thanked me for bringing them together.

I never saw or heard of the dog owner again. The local copper often dropped in at the bridge. We enjoyed a brew together and had a laugh about that fateful Spring Sunday when we encountered Cuddles, the dog man, the horse girl, and the Mini lad. Not forgetting 'Arry's contribution to the drama.

We could enjoy the laugh about the occurrences – but I still sincerely regret the demise of poor Cuddles and my part in it.

Not all the stories I accumulated came from the lads on the British canals and rivers. I spent some time in the USA and China on a Churchill Fellowship study tour of their waterways where I met some memorable characters. One man called Sam Brody particularly impressed me by his storytelling.

He reminded me so much in appearance and actions of my English mate 'Arry. He lived on his wits and hunted the wildlife for much of his food. Sam also traded with passing boats for the essentials of life.

Sam worked as a weather watcher and wildlife ranger on the Intercoastal waterways in the state of Louisiana. He lived on his own in a very remote cabin in the wilderness. There was no television and the only radio connection was with a base many miles away. I spent three days and nights with him due to a cock-up in my travel arrangements. It was the intention to only be with him for one day, but the tug that was to pick me up had engine trouble, hence the delay.

All around the cabin were dried skulls of the animals he had hunted. That was the first time I tasted alligator tail. Sam was amazing with a huge army fighting knife. I watched him skinning the 'Gator as he called it, using only the knife. The skin was dried and traded to passing boats, the end of the tail was cooked and the rest of the carcass was fed to his two hounds.

Hanging on the wall was a faded picture of him in army uniform. When I asked him about it he explained he had served in Vietnam most of the time as a 'tunnel rat'. When I enquired what that meant he avoided my query and moved on to another subject.

Sam was a fund of tales, my favorite being the story of when he was a kid and the antics of his granddad. Whether it is true or not is irrelevant – it was the story that counted.

His granddad was a veteran of the First World War. He had been an artillery spotter during his time in France and his duties entailed sitting in a wicker basket suspended below a hydrogen filled balloon. The balloon was attached by wire to a winch. It was flown near the battlefield, and his granddad reported by telephone the accuracy of the cannon fire.

The balloons were a prime target for the enemy air force and the death rate amongst the spotters was very high. His granddad was prone to depression and during these bouts he remembered his lost army mates and said he was only on borrowed time.

There had been a festival in the small town where they lived. The organizers had left in his granddad's garage a number of helium cylinders and a large advertising balloon to be picked up later. Sam had made it his business to drop in on his granddad a couple of times a week since his grandma died. He went one Saturday and couldn't find the old man in his house. He assumed he had gone out somewhere. He was about to leave on his bike when he saw a number of people looking towards his granddad's house. Just above the roof there appeared the balloon. Sam dropped his bike and went around to the back yard to find that his granddad had inflated the balloon. He had stretched a garden net over it and secured to the net was a wicker garden chair. In the chair was his granddad wearing his wartime leather coat and sporting his helmet and goggles. The chair was attached to a garden roller by a thin washing line. As the balloon rose the roller began to lift off the ground. His granddad was drunk as a lord and waved a bottle of rum at Sam when he recognized him. Sam ran across the yard and clung to the roller, pulling the contraption towards the earth. He landed the roller but the balloon was impossible to drag down.

His granddad shouted, "Let go, Sam. I'm off to join my comrades and my Hilda in heaven." Sam refused and pleaded with him not to do anything while he went for assistance. He tied the roller to a fence post with his belt. He had reached the front of the house and was asking the onlookers to help him when there was a gasp from the crowd. He turned around to see the balloon with his granddad slung underneath heading skyward. The old man had cut the rope. As he sailed up higher he waved to the crowd. He was whooping and a hollering then he started singing, "Up, up and away in my beautiful balloon..."

I asked, "What happened then, Sam?"

Sam said, "The stupid crowd cheered their bloody heads off. They thought it was some kind of publicity stunt."

I persisted, "I meant, what happened to your Granddad?"

"Oh he was all right, he was a born survivor, my old Grandpappy. The balloon came down in the next state. He was found by a television crew. You know those that report traffic congestion from a helicopter? Grandpappy was fast asleep hanging from a tree, not a scratch on him but with an almighty hangover. The mad bugger was a celebrity on all the TV channels for a few days."

I exclaimed, "Wow! That is some story, Sam. How is your Granddad, now?"

"Oh! Grandpappy is a long time dead. The day after they brought him home he was crossing the road. He got run down by a drunk driver. The very fella he had been drinking with all afternoon. That wasn't the first time he had done mad things, my

Grandpappy. No sir. I think he had tried to kill himself a few times. A lot of the guys that survived the war were never right in the head again. He was the last survivor of about six old veterans that used to meet up regular. They were out in a car together – the car ran into a river and two got drowned. That left four of them. They went hunting. Hunting! At their age, I ask you? A grizzly bear got one of them and ate the bugger. That left three. Number three got shot trying to stop a young junky holding up his son's liquor store. Just imagine a man of his age trying to stop a hold-up? When there was only two left out of the original gang that survived the war, their turn came next, they blew themselves up in a garden shed. His mate died but Grandpappy survived yet again."

"How did that happen?" I asked.

"Oh, they had a still and were brewing their own illegal liquor. When the sheriff questioned him Grandpappy reckons it just kinda went off with a bang. Lucky for us the Sheriff was an ex-serviceman and sympathised with the old vets. He kept things quiet. I have my own ideas but didn't say anything in case Grandpa got in trouble with the law."

"Why's that?" I enquired.

He informed me casually, "Oh! Because they had some explosives hidden in the shed. They used it when they went fishing."

Another good story for my collection. When I returned to civilization I was telling one of my American friends about my time with Sam. He was amazed that Sam had allowed me to stay over at his place. He explained, "Sam's a loner, that's why he chose that job out in the middle of nowhere. When he came back from the war his wife couldn't live with him. She said he had gone weird. Did he tell you what he did in Vietnam?"

I replied, "No. He mentioned something about 'tunnel rats'. I didn't understand and he seemed reluctant to tell me. I never pushed it."

He revealed, "I was in Vietnam myself. I reckon Sam had the worst job over there. Did you know the Viet Cong had tunnels all over the place?"

I replied, "Yes, I have heard about it. I believe they are a tourist attraction now."

He explained, "That's what Sam did. He went down the tunnels on his own and hunted the enemy. I believe he was missing down the tunnels for nearly a week on one occasion. Imagine that? No wonder he is a bit weird. I'll tell you something? I wouldn't have spent time alone with Sam for all the gold in Fort Knox."

I shuddered and replied, "Ignorance is bliss, eh?"

I frankly took the story with a pinch of salt until I was watching a TV programme entitled *Would you believe this?* in a hotel in the USA. The story of the old man's balloon flight featured in it.

Chapter Ten
The end of an era

THE DAY CAME when 'Arry decided he had worked long enough for the company. It seemed it was interfering with his other businesses. He asked to see me and I met up with him in the cabin of his boat. Although it was quite a hot summer's day he had the fire lit to boil his kettle. The cabin was stifling and after a few minutes I asked him if could we talk ashore on the towpath.

"No chance," he replied. "I dunna want them nosy sods to know my business."

I had to stick it out, sweating cobs.

The business he wanted to see me about was that he wanted to be included in the redundancy list the company was preparing, but secretly. Plus "Ow much dosh will I be getting?"

I attempted to explain the payment was calculated on service, earnings, age, etc.

He kept interrupting me by asking the same question again and again, totally ignoring my explanation. "But 'ow much dosh will I get? I got plans you see. I need to know 'ow much?"

In the end I gave up and invited him to the office, where all his records were kept, to discuss the matter. I then beat a hasty retreat before he could dream up another problem.

Prior to employees taking redundancy, all the workers that had opted to leave were invited to attend a personal interview along with their wives, husbands and partners. The meetings were arranged so that the benefits, regarding pensions and so on, could be explained to them.

A very genteel lady from Headquarters arrived to explain to the workers their rights, and also give financial advice if required. Many of the men at that time didn't have bank accounts and were paid in cash.

Part of my job was to try and explain the advantages of being paid via a bank and the use of a Switch card when shopping.

The lady from HQ informed me on her arrival that this was her first trip 'into the field' so to speak since she had completed her training. She was really looking forward to meeting the workers. I kept any remarks about the men to myself but inwardly thought, "Oh boy, Missus, have you got a good day ahead of you!"

One at a time the motley bunch came into the office. Although invited, some of the men refused to let their wives accompany them for fear that they would learn how much cash they would be receiving.

The queue gradually dwindled, the hours passed quite quickly and I was breathing sighs of relief as interviews progressed satisfactorily without any problems

I was sitting in on the interviews as the men's representative. Through the office window I observed the last couple, 'Arry accompanied by Cissie, waiting.

To honour the occasion, though dressed in his usual manner, 'Arry had a gaudy boatman's neckerchief knotted above the frayed collar of his once-white shirt.

Cissie wore a lurid flowered dress with a once-beautiful crocheted shawl draped over her thin shoulders. Securing the ends of the shawl across her scrawny chest was a very expensive-looking cameo brooch. Protruding from the uneven hemline of her dress, her spindly Olive Oyl legs were exaggerated by the enormous pair of brass-bound clogs she wore on her feet.

On her head, pulled well down over her ears, was a blue Tam o'Shanter crowned with a huge purple pompom.

The lady from HQ was having a pause and a welcome cup of tea between interviews. She remarked to me in the break that she had dealt with many people from all walks of life but had never come across... (there was a pause in her summarisation of the present clientele – she seemed to be choosing her words carefully

213

so as not to offend me) "...such an extraordinary bunch of colour-ful..."

She never finished her sentence. I was just about to explain to her that she had seen nothing yet, when the door burst open and in stomped 'Arry, dragging Cissie with him.

The lady was taken aback as 'Arry sat down before her demanding, "Now then, Missus, tell us 'ow much we are going to get! Mind, we want it now in proper money mind, cash, none of them cheque things. Don't trust them bloody banks. Me old fella told me about them collapsin' in the Thirties and I don't want nothing to do with them money-grabbin' sods."

The expression on the poor lady's face was a sight to behold. Evidently it was her first encounter with the likes of 'Arry and his wife.

'Arry continued, "Any writing and that, she can read, she knows her education, so don't try to kid us." He indicated Cissie who was in the process of adjusting her glasses in a very scholar-ly manner.

I decided it was time to intercede on behalf of the startled lady.

"'Arry, introduce yourself, this lady doesn't know who you are. She's here to help you, not fiddle you or Cissie."

'Arry grudgingly introduced himself and Cissie complaining, "Bloody office people – they tell you to come here and don't even know who you are."

Eventually the interview proceeded.

The lady began explaining the part 'Arry was really interested in. The cash pay-out. Calculating his entitlements on a sheet of paper she passed it over the desk for Cissie to read. 'Arry made a grab for the paper. After capturing it he snatched the glasses from Cissie's eyes. Unfortunately she had one of those strap attach-ments around her neck and she was jerked towards 'Arry. It was then that her Tam o'Shanter fell off. The lady and I sat back in amazement as Cissie's head was suddenly revealed.

One side of her head was almost completely bald, while on the other side her hair hung in greasy locks. Her right ear was rough-ly encased in a dirty blood-soaked bandage stuck to her head with long strips of equally dirty Elastoplast

After much arguing and cursing the couple settled down. Cissie with a look of triumph on her face was the obvious winner in the struggle for the glasses and paper even though she held it upside down as she pretended to study it. It was as he looked towards us, ready to pose yet a further question, that 'Arry must have observed the astonished expressions on our faces as we stared at his wife's strange hairdo.

He opened up. "Ha. What do you think of 'er 'ead? It's 'er own fault, she wouldn't keep still, silly cow, when I was cutting it last night. Always moaning she is. I only nicked her ear a bit. What a bloody 'to do' she made of it. You'd thought I was trying to murder 'er. I wouldn't mind but the bloody shears cost me a fortune off the sheep shearer fella."

Cissie, ashamed of her appearance and with attention focused on her, departed from the office in tears. Unconcerned about his wife's hasty retreat 'Arry waved us down when we attempted to follow her.

"She'll be all right. Bit touchy about 'er 'ead, that's all."

'Arry continued to question myself and the lady regarding his benefits.

Eventually the interview came to an end with the exhausted lady inviting him and his wife to a dinner the following week.

The company had laid this on as a parting gift to their redundant workers. This should be fun. "Er, I don't know, got a lot on at the minute. Summer, you see, lots of boats tying up by me pub."

I knew 'Arry was considering how much free ale he would possibly lose by not being at his favourite bar relating tales to the gullible tourists.

"Where is the shindig to be, then?" he inquired. I detected a touch of cunning in his question – something I have witnessed on a number of occasions as the old villain plotted the downfall of an innocent victim.

The nice lady explained, "It will be held at a nice hotel out in the country." 'Arry was impressed. He remarked. "Hotel! Not in an ale 'ouse then? Hmm. Is it a posh place, eh?"

She tried persuasion. "I'm sure your wife and you will enjoy the night out, 'Arry."

The nice lady told him where the hotel was located.

"Phew, Missus, can't get there. Can't drive you see, no car either."

I breathed a sigh of relief, this was an opportunity to prevent a disastrous occasion occurring. The lady pressed on with the invitation, resolving all problems as they arose. "Taxi, Harry," she beamed with triumph. "We will lay a taxi on to bring you and take you home."

"Would I 'ave to pay, Missus? Come hexpensive them taxis, so I'm told. Never bin in one, mind," he confessed with an innocence that made me shudder. She was falling for it and I was unable to warn her.

"No, the company will pay the fare."

Another pause as he considered what other concessions he could wheedle out of the nice lady.

"What about me ale, then? Aye! She likes her gin an' tonic as well, you know?" he pointed in the general direction of the door his poor wife had exited through.

The lady countered this demand with yet another foolish offer. Was this woman mad, I asked myself. Did she have any idea what she was letting us into? Would nobody rid me of this errant charitable nice lady?

"The company will buy your drinks, in fact the whole evening will cost you nothing, I can assure you," she beamed, sensing triumph.

At her last statement 'Arry surrendered and graciously agreed to attend. As I showed him out of the door he whispered, "Er, what kind of gear does we wear for this do, anyway? Sounds a bit of a posh place we are going to, eh?"

"Oh yes, sure is 'Arry, one of the smartest places around."

The truth was that I was still hoping to talk him out of attending and grasping at straws I imparted this information: "Best bib and tucker, me old mate. Got to be smart for the Last Supper, so to speak."

He thought for a moment, stroking his chin as usual when resolving a problem. "Free booze, she said, eh? As much as I can drink, eh? Um, that's OK. I know where me and the missus can get a nice get-up. See you, pal."

Off he went with an unaccustomed spring in his step. Oh God, what had we let ourselves in for?

The night of the meal arrived. All of the other invited employees and wives were already seated when 'Arry and Cissie appeared.

Having witnessed them after a session on the booze, and bearing in mind tonight there would be free drinks, I had deliberately reserved a small table located in an alcove for myself and the duo. 'Arry stood framed just inside the door looking around the assembled diners.

Gasps of surprise rippled around the room. His appearance amazed me. 'Arry was attired in a splendid dinner suit, a bit tight in places but still he had made the effort and put the rest of us to shame. The usually grubby shirt was also changed for a strange get-up with no collar but a stiff shiny front with a bow tie cellotaped in close proximity to his bulbous neck. He did however still wear his beloved cap which slightly spoiled his extraordinary apparel. 'Arry had even shaved for the occasion (I could see he had by the blood-soaked pieces of toilet paper adhering to his face).

He bellowed greetings to his mates as he strutted about obviously proud of his appearance. To all intents he looked like an old fashioned butler, with his large belly still supported by the wide leather belt, framed in the open lapels of the claw hammer coat with the shiny shirt front just about tucked under it. He had traded his steel toecap Wellies for a pair of black patent leather shoes, topped by a pair of startling white spats.

His workmates that knew him muttered to each other, drew their wives closer and shuffled nearer to their tables, leaving no room for 'Arry and Cissie to join them. Most of them had experienced drinking sessions with 'Arry and didn't fancy another one when free booze was in the offing, especially with their wives present. Others had heard of his reputation and cowered further into their seats hoping he wouldn't spot them. I leapt to my feet, rushed across to greet him and escorted him to the arranged table.

He greeted me with the words, "Now then, where's this 'ere free ale?" He scanned the restaurant, sniffing the air for a hint of beer smell. "Queer kind of ale 'ouse this, where's the bar?"

I greeted Cissie as she hid behind a huge potted plant, totally ignored by her husband. She appeared as if afraid to be seen in such a splendid place. Gently I took her arm and attempted to lead her to the table. At first she held back. I dodged behind the plant to persuade her, believing she was shy. Her appearance was equally as bizarre as her husband's. Her head was still encased in the strange Tam o'Shanter completely covering every shred of her remaining hair. It was her dress that dramatically changed her appearance. She wore a sequin-encrusted ballgown that completely covered her feet and probably the clogs she constantly wore.

"Let's go, Cissie – you look fantastic, you are the belle of the ball."

My statement appeared to give her the confidence to leave her hidey-hole. I collected 'Arry on the way to our place in the restaurant.

"Come on, 'Arry, we can have a drink when we are seated. No need to stand at a bar, they will bring the drinks to us. Come on, matey, the staff are waiting to serve the meal. This is the life eh? Waited on hand and foot!"

As we sat at the splendidly arranged table the lady from the head office decided to join us. Not a good idea for the uninitiated.

A waiter hovered close at hand to take our orders. The nice lady and I already had our drinks.

"A pre-dinner aperitif, Sir?" the waiter enquired. 'Arry looked baffled at his question. I whispered behind my hand. "He wants your drink order, 'Arry."

"Well, why the bloody 'ell didn't he say so? Aye lad, fetch me a pint of Guinness and the Missus 'ere a gin and tonic."

As the waiter was about to leave, 'Arry added, "Best bring us a couple of pints, lad, save your legs, eh?"

While we waited for the order to arrive 'Arry spotted the bottles of wine already placed on the table.

"So this is wine, eh? This is what the toffs drink all the time, eh?

Never tasted the stuff meself. I'm a beer man, me," he proudly
announced. "What's it like, anyway?"

Big mistake. The nice lady invited him to try a glass.

"Red or white Harry, I think you will like my choice. The red is
a nice Burgundy and the white is a cheeky little Riesling from
Germany. I discovered it when I went on a wine trail last year. Bit
of a hobby, wine is for me. My hubby and I go wine seeking every
year."

'Arry gave her a strange look as he accepted a glass of red.
Cissie, always at odds with her husband, sampled the white. They
quickly gulped them down and helped themselves to another
brimming glass just as the Guinness and gin and tonic arrived. I
could see the dilemma this put 'Arry into. He was doing his best
to impress the nice lady with his new-found manners. He made a
decision by holding a glass in either hand and taking a gulp of
Guinness and wine alternately. Cissie followed his example.

Yet another contribution to the nice lady's education.

The waiter presented us with menus. Standing close by he
waited for their orders. We had previously given our preferences.
Cissie and 'Arry studied them intently as the waiter impatiently
shuffled his feet. Aware that the duo couldn't read, I interceded to
save them from embarrassment.

"Hmm, I see they have some nice steaks on the menu. I like a
nice piece of steak myself, how about you two?"

They nodded in unison.

"How would Sir and Madam prefer their steak?" The waiter
enquired.

"On a plate, you silly bugger!" 'Arry responded with a look of
incredulity on his face.

I again interceded. "Make 'em both medium rare." I whispered
to the waiter.

"Melon, soup, or prawn cocktail?" he enquired. Another dilemma I spoke aloud as if studying the menu for myself. "What you
having, 'Arry?"

'Arry settled for the prawn cocktail, Cissie decided on the
melon. The waiter, impatient to take the orders to the kitchen,
extracted the menus from the pair while advising them. "I shall

bring the sweet trolley and cheeseboard around after your main course, Sir."

"Aye lad, and can you fetch me another couple of these?" 'Arry indicated the Guinness glasses. "And best top 'er up while yer at it, sunshine." He pointed at his wife. She was pouring into her glass the last of the cheeky little Riesling. The waiter removed the empty glasses and bottles then scurried for the kitchen. Up until then the nice lady and I had only the one drink we'd had before the couple arrived.

The wine waiter appeared, dressed in an evening suit with his little sample spoon hanging from a chain around his neck. He placed two more bottles of wine on the table. 'Arry admired his suit, stood up, did a pirouette and asked the man. "What do you think of my outfit?"

The man answered in a condescending voice, a slight sneer on his face, "I can honestly say, Sir, in all the years I have served in this establishment, I have never seen the likes of your, er, apparel before."

'Arry sat down, a self-satisfied smirk on his face, evidently content with the man's admiring response. Unfortunately the Dicky front slipped from underneath his belt and rolled up, spoiling 'Arry's display of his togs. He tried once or twice to tuck it in, gave up and ripped it off, muttering, "Bloody stupid thing, I told 'er it was no good. Too small, yer see?"

He relaxed with his bulging shirt front revealing a couple of missing buttons. The nice lady from HQ squirmed with embarrassment.

I had been dying to ask him a question and now saw the opportunity opened up by his conversation with the wine waiter. I chose my words carefully. It was not my intention to offend.

"Er, by the way, 'Arry, I kept meaning to ask you. Where did you and Cissie get your outfits? They are very posh, you put me to shame, I must say."

The nice lady leant forward, she was evidently intrigued also.

"The war, you see. Good times for us boaties."

He leaned back, belched, and revealed a period of his past life.

"I worked with the old fella then. We had a nice pair of boats each. We was in the Black Country waitin' for a cargo when the Germans bombed the place to shit, the bloody place was a wreck. But I can tell you this, there was lots of loot for the takin'. We went on the mooch, the old fella and me. Just up from where we was a-layin' a music hall had been hit by a bomb. All of one wall had been blowed out. Eh! Would you believe this? All over the road is clothes, every kind of gear you could think of. Me old fella grabbed this outfit. There's even a top hat to go with it as well. Didn't fancy wearin' that though. Anyway I was a-courtin' Cissie there at the time, so I grabs this 'ere dress she's a-wearin' now. Good, eh?" He added proudly.

"In fact, we got lots more gear stowed away in our 'ouse. I'll show yer when you're round our way if yer like."

"What a marvellous tale," the nice lady remarked admiringly. "The fact that you have kept it all these years is amazing."

"Had to, yer see, Missus. The old fella wanted to be buried in it."

"Oh, he's not dead then. Your father must be a ripe old age by now."

"Oh, aye, he's dead all right. That was his dying wish to be buried in this gear. He popped his clogs about ten years ago."

I had to ask, "Well, how come you still have the suit?"

He gave me a look of horror.

"What – and waste a bloody good outfit on that mean old sod? I want to get buried in it meself anyway, when me time comes. Eh! Cissie?" His wife nodded agreement.

"You see we had a bit of a fallin' out just before he snuffed it about some of his other gear. Tell you about it later – 'ere the ale's a'comin'."

The bar steward delivered the Guinness and gin and tonic. The nice lady began to look concerned. I became increasingly apprehensive. The starters arrived. Another double round of drinks was ordered. The nice lady was really looking *very* concerned.

Cissie watched the nice lady who also ordered the melon and followed her every move. She managed to handle the first course with dignity to the extent of even dabbing her mouth in unison with the nice lady. 'Arry on the other hand stared at the prawn cocktail with a puzzled look on his face.

"What's up, 'Arry?" I leaned over towards him, posing the question confidentially.

"What the bloody 'ell is this? I ordered one of them fancy cocktail things to drink. The silly sod has brought me a glass stuffed with rabbit food and worm things."

He poked at it with a dirty finger. "It's even got some kind of pink gravy on top. Yuk, I'm not touching this crap."

He took a hurried gulp of Guinness followed by a glass of wine. I knew it was useless trying to educate him in the culinary arts while he was consuming vast amounts of Irish baby maker and French dicky drooper. I advised him, "Ah! Don't bother with that, matey. You just enjoy your booze until the main course arrives."

I managed to pour myself the last glass of red wine as he reached for the bottle. The wine waiter appeared as if by magic, setting down two more bottles of wine. 'Arry attempted to order more Guinness.

"I shall inform the bar steward for you, Sir. I am the Maître D. Beer is not my department."

'Arry sneered as he departsed, "Big soft tart!"

The starter plates were cleared and the main course arrived along with another round of drinks.

Four large slightly pink steaks adorned our plates, the preferred choice of us all. Vegetables were delivered in dishes arranged around the table.

Cissie's disappearance under the table startled me until she reappeared with a huge toothy grin on her face. 'Arry sat glumly staring at his plate as we tucked in. Cissie loaded her plate with a variety of potatoes and veg, omitting nothing.

"First time I've ever been for a cooked sit-down meal," she revealed to the nice lady. Although I was eating and enjoying my meal, I noticed 'Arry had made no move to begin. Fearing he didn't like the steak meal either I asked him if there was a problem.

"Only problem is 'er sitting over there. Greedy cow, look at the way she's a-showing off. Come on, Cissie, my turn."

Oh. Oh. I had a feeling we were about to become involved in yet another of the strange couple's rituals. Cissie continued to chew on pieces of steak, a look of supreme happiness on her worn face. 'Arry was getting angrier by the minute until he exploded: "Right, Cissie, this is your last chance. My turn and I mean it."

At last he appeared to frighten her into some kind of submission. Again she disappeared under the table at the same time he dived under. She reappeared and sat back glumly in her chair, not attempting to continue her meal. 'Arry reappeared with a mouthful of gleaming gnashers and systematically began to demolish his steak and everything else on the table. The nice lady, baffled by Cissie's change of attitude to the meal, asked her if there was there a problem.

"Only problem is 'im over there, he's got both sets and won't give them up until he's finished," she smiled resignedly, revealing a mouth bereft of teeth. This last antic was too much for the nice lady who made a feeble excuse and departed towards the Ladies in haste.

The evening continued in a similar vein with only me keeping the duo company. 'Arry revealed why he had fallen out with his father on his deathbed. It appeared the vindictive old man had left the bottom set of his false teeth to Cissie and the top set to 'Arry. They were only ever able to eat anything but mush food until each one agreed to relinquish their inheritance to the other.

I had heard the story of the inherited teeth from my workmates and had found it hard to believe until I personally witnessed it.

We were the last to leave the restaurant, 'Arry hanging on to the privilege of free booze until the staff began turning lights out. I assisted the pair with difficulty into a taxi. The inebriated couple sang their hearts out all the way home – mostly sentimental wartime songs – except for a couple of stops for 'Arry to relieve himself.

I joined him behind a churchyard hedge where he divulged another aspect of his strange life confidentially to me. It was a medical problem.

He confessed to me in a whisper. "'Cos I got a bit of proste, thingy trouble you see, I gotta go when I want to. Doctor told me when I went to see him.

"I was 'avin' trouble peeing, yer see. You know, Scouse, and I hope you don't have the same trouble – the quacks stick their finger up your arse! Bloody murder that is, I'm telling you. You know the other doctor in our surgery is a woman. Imagine having to show your arse to a woman!"

'Arry shuddered at the thought.

"Oh, Scouse, no mention of it to Cissie, she don't know, so don't let on to 'er, you 'ear."

He leaned even closer presumably so Cissie couldn't hear, even though she was still in the taxi a good distance away.

"See, if she knows she will get worried about her sex life, yer see. Always been very active in that department, has our Cissie," he added proudly.

The idea of 'Arry and Cissie pounding away, 'Arry still wearing his cap and boots, her still wearing her clogs, surrounded by their animals, made me shudder and giggle at the same time.

He revealed other details of his complaint. "See, first of all you can't pee, then when you get it going the bloody thing won't stop."

Stupid me, I thought his constant trips to the toilet were something to do with the gallons of Guinness and wine he had consumed at the dinner.

I'd heard enough about 'Arry's dangly bit problems and headed back towards the taxi. I did however keep an eye on him in case he decided to settle down for the night amongst the graves.

I saw them to their cottage safely before making my own way home. 'Arry was unable to find the keyhole in his paralytic state. I opened the door to be greeted by his menagerie of animals. Assisting the pair of them inside before I could find the light switch, I stood on something soft and hairy that squealed a protest. Vacating the premises at speed, I slammed the door and bolted for the taxi.

A month or so later I heard they had given up their canalside cottage. 'Arry had purchased a surplus narrow boat with his redundancy cash. The boat was without luxuries, in fact still rigged as a basic trade boat. This would be as she was when the two of them had spent their lives, living and working on them. My last report of the couple was from a pleasure boat crew that had spent the night close to them somewhere down south. They had been entertained in a lock-side pub by 'Arry's tales of life on the cut. His *pièce de resistance* had been however his story of a meal he had partaken of in a very posh restaurant – drinking as much free ale as he could, served up by a gang of poofters dressed up like dogs' dinners.

The rest of the lads went their separate ways. I stayed in touch with a few. We met up on occasions either in my house or at the retired employees' Christmas dinner.

Big Al found a job on a stately home estate driving tractors and lawn mowers, and looking after the bees.

Puddling Paul rejoined the circus. I see him when he visits the region.

Jacko got himself a job in the council gardening department.

Brickie is a freelance jobber doing house repairs. Sam works with him as his labourer.

The other men? Unfortunately I lost touch with them.

Not long after 'Arry's departure from the waterways my health deteriorated and I had to take early retirement. At first it seemed like heaven, getting up when I wanted to instead of being ruled by the clock. It was bliss not having other people's problems to deal with.

Very shortly I became bored out of my skull. I missed the lads and the incredible debates. You can only do so many crosswords and watch so much TV before life becomes mind-numbing.

That is when I made a decision to take up writing...

Also from Léonie Press:

MEMORIES OF A CHESHIRE CHILDHOOD - MEMORIAL EDITION
Lenna Bickerton (ISBN 978-1-901253-13-9)
Lenna describes life in Northwich around the First World War through the sharp senses of a child. Her memories are vivid: duck eggs for breakfast, dancing to Grandad's gramophone, a near tragedy at a watermill, her schooldays, the sights and sounds of the old town, the smells of wild flowers, busy boat traffic on the canal — and the menacing "Ginny Greenteeth." This memorial edition includes her obituary. **£4.99**

NELLIE'S STORY – *A Life of Service*
Elizabeth Ellen Osborne (ISBN 978-1-901253-15-3)
Elizabeth Ellen Osborne was born at Shipbrook, near Northwich, Cheshire, in 1914. Her father was a farm worker and the family lived in a tied cottage. When she left school at 14 she went into service for the local 'toffs'. Following her marriage she was a nurse, a 'dinner lady' and a much-loved foster mother. As a Royal British Legion welfare officer she rode round Mid-Cheshire on a 90cc motorcycle until she was 80. **£5.99**

DIESEL TAFF – *From 'The Barracks' to Tripoli*
Austin Hughes (ISBN 978-1-901253-14-6)
Austin Hughes was born in February 1922 at 'The Barracks', a group of flea-ridden cottages deep in rural North Wales. From childhood he had loved heavy machinery and he learned to drive trucks and bulldozers. Then in 1940 he was called up to join the Royal Engineers. This was to be an experience which changed the young Welshman's life and earned him his nick-name 'Diesel Taff'. By the end of the war, he'd driven thousands of miles across deserts and mountains, transporting heavy plant, building roads and air strips, clearing avalanches and ferrying refugees. **£8.99**

BEYOND THE STILE - *A Cheshire Lad Remembers*
Ken Wilbraham (ISBN 978-1-901253-46-7)
Ken Wilbraham remembers his post-war childhood growing up in the village of Guilden Sutton near Chester, where a child's paradise lay beyond the stile and his caring parents' chaotic home was full of his eccentric father's unfinished projects. **£8.99**

INNS OF PRESCOT AND WHISTON
Mavis Abraham and W K Blinkhorn (ISBN 978-1-901253-44-3)
A study of the inns, hotels, public houses and taverns in Prescot and Whiston from the 16th century to the 1990s. **£3.50**

Visit our website www.leoniepress.com to see our selection of books about Cheshire and other autobiographies.

Also from Léonie Press:

HAPPY DAYS AND HEARTBREAK DAYS
A farmer's son relives his 1920s childhood
Victor William Dilworth (ISBN 978-1-901253-34-4)

A gem of rural English social history written through the innocent and curious eyes of a toddler and small boy, this book tells of the author's childhood on a Shropshire farm. Victor was the youngest of a large family, whose busy parents had little time for him until he could do some useful work. But he absorbed everything that was going on around him and asked endless questions. **£6.99**

PINAFORE STREET - A Fenland childhood
Kathleen Lord (ISBN 978-1-901253-39-9)

In vivid and witty detail, Kathleen Lord describes her childhood in Boston, Lincolnshire in the years after the First World War, bringing a long-gone era sharply into focus. Nearly 90 when the book was published, her memoirs were written after she retired about 30 years ago and will be read with nostalgic pleasure by her contemporaries and with great interest by those who love social history. **£6.99**

CHESHIRE FOLK SONGS & ASSOCIATED TRADITIONS
Roy Clinging (ISNB 978-1-901253-49-8)

Folk musician Roy Clinging has compiled and edited a collection of 60 songs from his native Cheshire, which are published here together with explanatory notes. Fifty of the songs are printed with their music and a practise/audition CD is available to accompany the book which will help those who prefer to learn their melodies by ear. **£11.99**

IT'S MUCK YOU WANT!
The humorous story of a double life
Jack Orrell (ISBN 978-1-901253-41-2)

Retired optician Jack Orrell writes of the hectic years after WW2 when he and his wife turned a rundown Shropshire farm (previously condemned by the war Agricultural Committee for bad husbandry) into a model example of modern farming techniques. He commuted a daily 70-mile round trip to continue working as an optician at Ellesmere Port and spent all the rest of the day as a farmer. The author's royalties will go to Cancer Research UK. **£8.99**

OWNERS, OCCUPIERS AND OTHERS - 17th century Northwich
Tony Bostock (ISBN 978-1-901253-37-5)

A detailed book by a leading local historian about life in Northwich, Cheshire during the 17th century - a time of great religious, social, political and economic change. **£10.99**

Visit our website www.leoniepress.com to see our selection of books about Cheshire and other autobiographies.

By the same author:

THE ANGELS OF MONS

Carl Leckey

Published in New
Zealand by National
Pacific Press

CARL LECKEY's first book, "The Angels of Mons", was published in 2004 in New Zealand – where his children now live and where he and his wife spend a lot of their time.

It is an immensely moving novel about the horrors of the First World War, and the hero is a resourceful under-age soldier who, like Carl's own grandfather, is put into the Labour Corps. He is initially given the ghastly task of burying the battlefield dead and the body parts left over from field surgery, then graduates to becoming an ambulance driver, working with brave "conchie" stretcher-bearers. One of them becomes his mentor.

The detail in the book is so extraordinarily vivid that Carl feels the story was "channelled" through him by a dead stretcher-bearer as a means of bringing these terrible experiences out into the public domain.

Most old soldiers have understandably avoided describing such painful and squalid circumstances in their memoirs about the Great War – but the horrors they endured should be more widely known and understood.

"The Angels of Mons" was originally published by National Pacific Press in New Zealand but is now available from Léonie Press, 13 Vale Road, Hartford, Northwich, Cheshire CW8 1PL, price £9.99 plus £2.58 post and package.